*POPULAR LECTURES IN MATHEMATICS SERIES*

Editors: I. N. Sneddon and M. Stark

---

## Volume 4

# GEOMETRICAL CONSTRUCTIONS
# USING COMPASSES ONLY

*TITLES IN THE POPULAR LECTURES IN MATHEMATICS SERIES*

# GEOMETRICAL CONSTRUCTIONS USING COMPASSES ONLY

*by*

## A. N. KOSTOVSKII

*Translated from the Russian by*
### HALINA MOSS, B.Sc.

*Translation Editor*
### IAN N. SNEDDON
Simson Professor of Mathematics
in the University of Glasgow

## BLAISDELL PUBLISHING COMPANY
### NEW YORK · LONDON
### A DIVISION OF RANDOM HOUSE

SOLE DISTRIBUTORS IN THE UNITED STATES AND CANADA
Blaisdell Publishing Company
22 East 51st Street, New York 22, N.Y.

A translation of the original volume
*Geometricheskiye postroyeniya odnim tsirkulem*
(Moscow, Fizmatgiz, 1959)

Library of Congress Card Number: 61-11527

*Printed in Great Britain by Pergamon Printing and Art Services Limited, London*

# C O N T E N T S

## P A R T   1

### CONSTRUCTIONS WITH COMPASSES ALONE

## P A R T   2

### GEOMETRIC CONSTRUCTIONS BY MEANS OF COMPASSES ALONE BUT WITH RESTRICTIONS

v

# CONTENTS

# FOREWORD

The author of the present article has on many occasions given lectures on the theory of geometrical constructions to participants in mathematical olympiads, which have been organized every year since 1947, for the pupils of secondary schools in the city of Lvov. These lectures served as a foundation for the writing of the first part of this work.

The second part consists of investigations made by the author in connexion with geometrical constructions carried out with a limited opening of the 'legs'.

The present article is written for a wide circle of readers. It should help teachers and pupils of senior classes of secondary schools to acquaint themselves in greater detail with geometrical constructions carried out with the help of compasses alone. This work can serve as a teaching aid in the work of school mathematical clubs. It can also be used by students studying elementary mathematics in physics and mathematics departments of teachers' training colleges and universities.

The author wishes to express his sincere thanks to A.S. Kovanko, W.F. Rogachenko and I.F. Teslenko who read the manuscript carefully and offered a great deal of valuable advice.

# INTRODUCTION

Geometrical constructions form a substantial part of a mathematical education. They represent a powerful tool of geometrical investigations.

The tradition of limiting the tools of geometrical construction to a ruler and compasses goes back to remote antiquity.

The famous geometry of Euclid (3rd century B.C.) was based on geometrical constructions carried out by compasses and a ruler, the compasses and ruler being regarded as equivalent instruments; it was a matter of indifference how each separate construction was carried out - by means of the compasses and the ruler, or by means of the compasses alone or by means of the ruler alone.

It was noted a long time ago that compasses are a more exact, a more perfect instrument than a ruler. It was observed too that certain constructions could be carried out by means of compasses, without the use of a ruler; for example, to divide a circumference into six equal parts, to construct a point symmetrical to a given point with respect to a given straight line, and so on. Attention was drawn to the fact that in engraving thin metal plates, in marking the dividing circles on astronomical instruments as a rule only compasses are used. The latter, probably, gave the impetus to investigations on geometrical constructions carried out by compasses alone.

In the year 1797, the Italian mathematician Lorenzo Mascheroni, professor of the University of Pavia, published a large work 'The Geometry of Compasses', which was later translated into French and German. In that work the following proposition was proved:

<u>All construction problems soluble by means of compasses and a ruler can also be solved exactly by means of compasses alone.</u>

# INTRODUCTION

This statement was proved in 1890 by A. Adler in an original way, using inversion. He also proposed a general method of solving geometrical construction problems by means of compasses alone. In 1928, the Danish mathematician Hjelmslev found in a bookshop in Copenhagen a book by G. Mohr ('The Danish Euclid') published in 1672 in Amsterdam. In the first part of this book there is a full solution of Mascheroni's problem. Thus, it had been shown a long time before Mascheroni that all geometrical constructions capable of being carried out with compasses and a ruler can be carried out by means of compasses alone.

The division of geometry in which geometrical constructions by means of compasses alone are studied is called 'The Geometry of the Compasses'. In 1833 the Swiss geometer Jacob Steiner published the work 'Geometrical Construction Carried out with the Aid of a Straight Line and a Fixed Circle', in which he investigated most fully constructions carried out with the ruler alone. The basic result of this work can be formulated as follows:

Every construction problem, soluble by means of compasses and a ruler, can be solved by means of a ruler alone, provided that in the plane of the drawing there is a given circle with fixed centre and radius.

Thus, in order to make the ruler equivalent to the compasses, it is sufficient to use the compasses once.

The great Russian mathematician N.I. Lobachevskii, in the first half of the 19th century, discovered a new geometry, which later became known as non-Euclidean geometry or Lobachevskian geometry. Recently, thanks to the efforts of a great number of scholars, especially Soviet ones, the theory of geometrical constructions in Lobachevskian geometry has been vigorously developed.

A.S. Smogorzhevskii, V.F. Rogachenko, K.K. Mokrishchev and other mathematicians have carried out investigations into constructions in the Lobachevskian plane without a ruler, showing the possibility of executing constructions similar to the constructions of Mascheroni in the Euclidean plane.

The great number of general investigations led to the formulation in the works of our scholars of quite a full and

exact theory of geometrical constructions in the Lobachevskian plane, scarcely inferior in its completeness to the
theory of geometrical constructions in the Euclidean plane.

# Part 1

## Constructions with compasses alone

# 1. ON THE POSSIBILITY OF SOLVING GEOMETRICAL CONSTRUCTION PROBLEMS BY MEANS OF COMPASSES ALONE: THE BASIC THEOREM

In this section the proof of the basic theorem of the Geometry of Compasses will be prescribed. To do so, it is necessary to examine the solutions of certain problems on construction with compasses alone.

It is clear that we cannot, with compasses alone, draw a continuous straight line given by two points on it, although we shall show later how, using compasses alone, we can construct one, two, and, generally, any number of points, situated as closely together as desired on a given straight line*.

Thus, the construction of a straight line is not fully covered by the Mohr-Mascheroni theory.

In the geometry of compasses, a straight line or a segment is defined by two points and is not given as a continuous straight line (drawn with a ruler). The construction of a straight line is regarded as completed as soon as any two points on it are constructed.

Let us agree to write the phrase 'With point $A$ as centre and radius $BC$ we describe a circle (or draw an arc)' in the short form: 'We describe the circle $(A, BC)$' or 'We draw the circle $(A, BC)$', or, shorter still, 'We describe $(A, BC)$'. Instead of the notation $(A, AB)$ we shall write $(A, B)$.

For the sake of clarity, we shall still mark (in dots) straight lines in the diagrams. (These straight lines play no part in the constructions).

Problem 1. To construct a point, symmetrical to a given point with respect to the given straight line $AB$.

---

*From the practical point of view, there is no ground to regard a straight line as constructed, if some of its points are constructed.

C o n s t r u c t i o n. We describe the circles $(A, C)$ and $(B, C)$ , i.e. using the points $A$ and $B$ as centres, we draw circles passing through the point $C$ (Fig. 1). At the intersection of these circles we obtain point $C_1$ . The point $C_1$ is the required one.

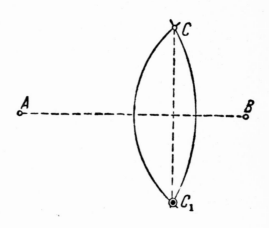

Fig. 1

N o t e. To verify that three points $A$, $B$ and $X$ lie on one straight line, it is necessary to construct any point $C$ outside the straight line and then the point $C_1$ , symmetrical to $C$. Obviously, the point $X$ lies on the straight line $AB$ if the segments $CX$ and $C_1X$ are equal to each other (Fig. 1).

Problem 2. To construct a segment, 2, 3, 4, ... and, in general, $n$ times greater than a given segment $AA_1 = r$ (where $n$ is any natural number).

C o n s t r u c t i o n. (Method 1). Keeping the opening of the compasses constant and equal to $r$ we describe the circle $(A_1, r)$ and we construct the point $A_2$, diametrically opposite to the point $A$, for which purpose we mark off the chords $AB = BC = CA_2 = r$ (Fig. 2). The segment $AA_2 = 2r$. We then describe the circle $(A_2, r)$ which intersects the circle $(C, r)$ at the point $D$. At the point of intersection of the circles $(D, r)$ and $(A_2, r)$ we obtain the point $A_3$. The segment $AA_3 = 3r$, and so on. Having carried out the indicated constructions $n$ times we construct the segment $AA_n = nr$. The validity of the construction follows from the fact that compasses with an opening equal to the radius of a circle divide its circumference into 6 equal parts.

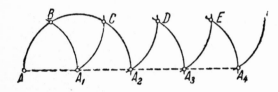

Fig. 2

Construction. (Method 2). We take any point $B$ outside $AA_1$ and we draw the circles $(A_1, AB)$ and $(B, r)$, which meet at the point $C$ (Fig. 3).

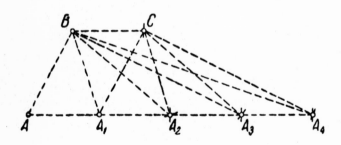

Fig. 3

If the circles $(A_1, r)$ and $(C, BA_1)$ are drawn they will intersect in the point $A_2$. The segment $AA_2 = 2r$. Describing the circles $(A_2, r)$ and $(C, BA_2)$ we obtain the point $A_3$ . The segment $AA_3 = 3r$, and so on.

The validity of this construction follows immediately from the fact that the figures $ABCA_1$, $A_1BCA_2$, $A_2BCA_3$, ... are parallelograms.

<u>Problem 3</u>. <u>Construct the fourth proportional to three given segments, $a$, $b$ and $c$.</u>

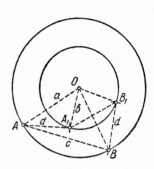

Fig. 4

C o n s t r u c t i o n  in the case, when $c < 2a$ :  With any point $O$ in the plane  as the centre, we describe two concentric circles of radii $a$ and $b$ (Fig. 4). On the circle $(O, a)$ we mark off the chord $AB = c$, then, with an arbitrary radius $d$ we describe two circles, $(A, d)$ and $(B, d)$, which intersect the circle $(O, b)$ at the points $A_1$ and $B_1$ . The segment $A_1B_1$ is the required fourth proportional to the three given segments.

P r o o f.  The triangles $AOA_1$ and $BOB_1$ are equal, having all corresponding sides equal, therefore $\angle AOA_1 = \angle BOB_1$ Hence $\angle AOB = \angle A_1OB_1$ and the isosceles triangles $AOB$ and $A_1OB_1$ are similar. It follows that

$$a:b = c:A_1B_1.$$

C o n s t r u c t i o n  i n  t h e  c a s e  o f $c \geqslant 2a$ .  In the case of $b < 2a$ , we construct the fourth proportional of the segments $a$, $c$ and $b$ . Otherwise, we

construct the segment  $na$  (Problem 2), taking $n$ such that
$c < 2na$   (or $b < 2na$))*.

We construct a segment  $y$ , the fourth proportional to the
segments  $na$ , $b$  and  $c$ . If, now, we construct a segment
$x = ny$  (Problem 2) then we obtain a segment, which is a
fourth proportional to the three given segments  $a$, $b$  and  $c$ .

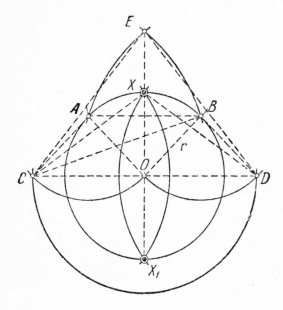

Fig. 5

Indeed

$$na:b = c:y$$

or

$$a:b = c:ny.$$

*We find a segment $2na > c$ in the following way.  We construct
the segment  $a_1 = 2a$  (Problem 2). From an arbitrary point $O_1$,
in the plane, we describe a circle $(O_1, c)$ and we measure off
in an arbitrary direction segments $O_1A_1 = a_1$, $O_1A_2 = 2a_1$, $O_1A_3 = 3a_1$ ,
etc. (Problem 2).   After a finite number of steps we arrive
at the point $A_n$ which will lie outside of the circle  $(O_1, c)$.
Obviously, the segment $O_1A_n = na_1 = 2na > c$.

### Problem 4. To divide the arc *AB* of a circle in half.

C o n s t r u c t i o n. We can assume that the centre *O* of the circle is known; it will be shown below (Problem 13) how to construct the centre of a circle (or arc) using compasses alone.

Putting $OA = OB = r$ and $AB = a$ , we describe circles $(O, a)$, $(A, r)$ and $(B, r)$; at the intersection we obtain the points *C* and *D* (Fig. 5).

We draw the circles $(C, B)$ and $(D, A)$ up to their intersection at the point *E* . If, now, the circles $(C, OE)$ and $(D, OE)$ be drawn, then, at their intersection, we obtain points *X* and $X_1$. The point *X* divides in half the arc *AB* , the point $X_1$ divides the arc that completes, with the first one, the full circle. In the case when the whole circle $(O, A)$ is drawn, we need draw only one of the two circles $(C, OE)$ and $(D, OE)$, which, at its intersection with the circle $(O, A)'$, will define points *X* and $X_1$ .

P r o o f. The figures *ABOC* and *ABDO* are parallelograms; therefore, the points *C*, *O* and *D* lie on the same straight line $(CO \parallel AB, OD \parallel AB)$. It follows from the isosceles triangles *CED* and *CXD* that $\sphericalangle COE = \sphericalangle COX = 90°$ . Thus the segment *OX* is perpendicular to the chord *AB* . Consequently, in order to prove that the point *X* divides the arc *AB* in half, it is sufficient to show that the segment

$$OX = r.$$

It follows from the parallelogram *ABOC* that

$$OA^2 + BC^2 = 2OB^2 + 2AB^2$$

or

$$r^2 + BC^2 = 2r^2 + 2a^2,$$

so that

$$BC^2 = 2a^2 + r^2$$

From the right-angled triangle *COE* we have

$$CE^2 = BC^2 = OC^2 + OE^2,$$

whence

$$2a^2 + r^2 = a^2 + OE^2$$

and

$$OE^2 = a^2 + r^2.$$

Finally, from the right-angled triangle $COX$ we obtain

$$OX = \sqrt{CX^2 - OC^2} = \sqrt{OE^2 - OC^2} =$$
$$= \sqrt{a^2 + r^2 - a^2} = r.$$

As we have already pointed out, in the geometry of the compasses a straight line is regarded as constructed as soon as any two of its points are defined. In our further discussions (Problems 24, 25 and others) we shall have to construct, with compasses alone, one, two and, in general, any number of points of the given straight line. This construction can be carried out as follows:

Problem 5. <u>On a straight line, defined by two points $A$ and $B$, construct one or several points</u>.

C o n s t r u c t i o n. We take an arbitrary point $C$ (Fig. 6) in the plane, outside the straight line $AB$ . We

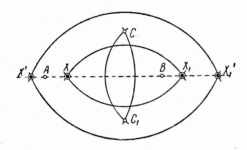

Fig. 6

construct a point, $C_1$ , symmetrical to $C$ with respect to $AB$ (Problem 1). With an arbitrary radius $r$ , we describe the circles $(C, r)$ and $(C_1, r)$ . At their intersection we obtain the required points $X$ and $X_1$ , which lie on the straight line $AB$ . Varying the size of the radius $r$ , it is possible to construct any number of points of the given straight line: $X', X_1'$ , etc.

Problem 6. <u>Construct the points of intersection of the</u>

given circle $(O, r)$ and the straight line, given by two points $A$ and $B$ .

C o n s t r u c t i o n in the case, when the centre $O$ does not lie on the given straight line $AB$ (Fig. 7)*. We construct the point $O_1$, symmetrical to the centre $O$ of the given circle, with respect to the straight line $AB$ (Problem 1). We describe the circle $(O_1, r)$ which intersects with the given circle at the required points $X$ and $Y$ .

The truth of the construction is obvious from the symmetry of the figure with respect to the given straight line $AB$ .

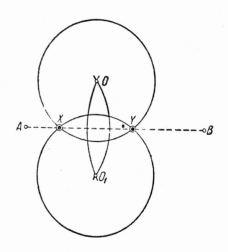

Fig. 7

C o n s t r u c t i o n  in the case when the centre $O$ of the given circle lies on the straight line $AB$ (Fig. 8).

With $A$ as the centre and an arbitrary radius $d$ , we describe a circle, which intersects the given circle at the points $C$ and $D$ . We halve the arcs $CD$ of the circle $(O, r)$ (Problem 4).

*With the help of compasses alone it is easy to check whether three given points lie on one straight line or not (see note to Problem 1).

The points $X$ and $Y$ are the required ones.

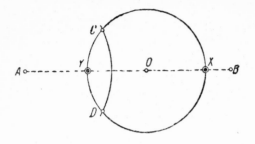

Fig. 8

N o t e .  From the construction discussed above it follows that

$$AX = AO + OX \quad \text{and} \quad AY = AO - OX.$$

Problem 7.  To construct the point of intersection of two straight lines $AB$ and $CD$, each of which is given by two points.

C o n s t r u c t i o n .  We construct points $C_1$ and $D_1$, symmetrical to $C$ and $D$ respectively, with respect to the given straight line $AB$ (Fig. 9). We describe circles $(D_1, CC_1)$

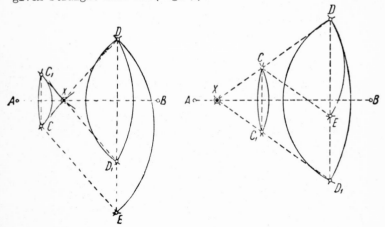

Fig. 9

and $(C, D)$ and we denote the point of their intersection by
$E$ . We construct the segment $x$ , fourth proportional to the
segments $DE, DD_1$ , and $CD$ (Problem 3). Now, if the circles
$(D, x)$ and $(D_1, x)$ are drawn, we then obtain the required point
$X$ at their intersection.

P r o o f. As the point $C_1$ is symmetrical to the point
$C$ , and the point $D_1$ is symmetrical to the point $D$ , then,
obviously, we shall find the point of intersection of the
given straight lines  if we construct the point of intersection of the straight lines $CD$ and $C_1D_1$ .

The figure $CC_1D_1E$ is a parallelogram, consequently,  the
points $D, D_1$ and $E$ lie on the same straight line $(DE \| CC_1,\ DD_1 \|$
$CC_1)$.    The triangles $CDE$ and $XDD_1$ are similar, therefore

$$DE:DD_1 = CE:D_1X,$$

but

$$CE = CD = C_1D_1.$$

The segment $D_1X = x$ is the fourth proportional of the segments $DE, DD_1$ and $CD$ .

Each constructional problem with compasses and a ruler in
the Euclidean plane is always reducible to the solution in
a definite order of the following very simple basic problems:

1.  To draw a straight line through two given points.

2.  To describe a circle of a given radius from a given
    centre.

3.  To find the points of intersection of two given circles.

4.  To find the points of intersection of a given circle
    with a straight line given by two points.

5.  To find the point of intersection of two straight lines,
    each of which is given by two points.

In order to prove that any construction problem which can
be solved with a ruler and compasses can also be solved by
means of compasses alone, it is sufficient to show  that all
these basic operations can be carried out by means of compasses alone.

The second and third operations are carried out directly

by compasses. The remaining basic operations were carried
out in Problems 5-7.

Suppose that a certain construction problem, soluble by
means of compasses and a ruler, has to be solved by means
of compasses alone. Let us imagine this problem solved by
means of a ruler and compasses. As a result, the solution
is reduced to carrying out a certain finite sequence of the
five basic operations. Having carried out each of these
operations with compasses alone (Problems 5-7) we arrive at
the solution of the original problem.

Thus all construction problems, soluble by means of compasses and a ruler, can be solved exactly by means of compasses alone.

The method of solving geometrical construction problems
by means of compasses alone leads, as a rule, to quite comp-
licated and lengthy constructions, but it has great interest
from the theoretical point of view.

## 2. SOLUTION OF GEOMETRICAL CONSTRUCTION PROBLEMS
BY MEANS OF COMPASSES ALONE

In this section we shall discuss the solution of certain
interesting problems in the geometry of compasses, arrived
at mainly by the efforts of Mohr, Mascheroni and Adler.
The solutions of some of these problems will be used in the
second part.

Problem 8. <u>To draw a perpendicular to the segment $AB$ at
the point $A$</u> .

C o n s t r u c t i o n. (First Method). Keeping the
opening of the compasses constant and equal to an arbitrary
segment $r$ , we draw the circles $(A, r)$ and $(B, r)$ until they
meet at the point $O$ . We describe the circle $(O, r)$ and we
construct the point $E$ on it, which is diametrically opposite
to the point $B$ . For this we draw the chords $CD = DE = r$
(Fig. 10), where $C$ is the point of intersection of the circles $(B, r)$ and $(O, r)$ . The segment $AE$ is perpendicular to
$AB$ . If we put $r = AB$ , then $AE = \sqrt{3}\, AB$ , and the point $C$
coincides with the point $A$ .

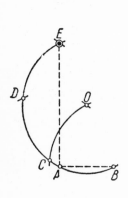

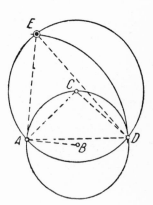

Fig. 10               Fig. 11

C o n s t r u c t i o n.  (Second Method). We describe
the circumference $(B, \quad A)$ (Fig. 11), we take an arbitrary
point $C$ on it and we draw the circle $(C, A)$. Let $D$ be the
point at which these circles intersect. If now a third
circle $(A, D)$ is drawn to its intersection with the circle
$(C, A)$ at the point $E$, then the segment $AE$ is perpendicular
to $AB$.

P r o o f. The segment $AC$ joins the centres of the circles
$(A, D)$ and $(C, A)$. $DE$ is their common chord; this means that
$AC$ is perpendicular to $DE$ and $\angle CAD = \angle CAE$ (the triangle
$ADE$ is equilateral).

On the other hand $\angle CAD = \angle ADC = \dfrac{\smile AC}{2}$. It follows from
the last equations that

$$\angle CAE = \frac{\smile AC}{2}.$$

The straight line $AE$ is the tangent to the circle $(B, \quad A)$ at
the point $A$, so that $AE$ is perpendicular to $AB$.

Problem 9. To construct a segment, equal to $\dfrac{1}{n}$ of a given
segment $AB$ (to divide the segment $AB$ into $n$ equal parts,
$n = 2, 3, \ldots$).

C o n s t r u c t i o n.  (First Method). We construct the
segment $AC = nAB$ (Problem 2). We describe the circle $(C, A)$.
At the intersection with the circle $(A, B)$ we obtain the
points $D$ and $D_1$. The circles $(D, A)$ and $(D_1, A)$ define the point
$X$ such that the segment $AX = \dfrac{AB}{n}$ (Fig. 12).

Increasing the segment $AX$ 2, 3, and so on, $n$ times (Problem 2), we construct the points which divide the segment
$AB$ into $n$ equal parts.

P r o o f. From the similarity of the isosceles triangles
$ACD$ and $AXD$ (the angle $A$ is a common one) it follows that

$$AC : AD = AD : AX$$

or

$$AD^2 = AB^2 = AC \cdot AX = nAB \cdot AX.$$

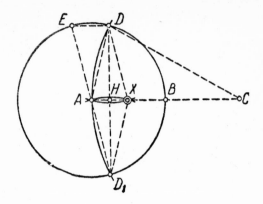

Fig. 12

Hence

$$AX = \frac{1}{n} AB.$$

The point $X$ lies on the straight line $AB$.

N o t e. For large values of $n$, the point $X$ is poorly defined; the arcs of the circles $(D, A)$ and $(D_1, A)$ intersect at $X$ at a very small angle*. In this case, to define the point $X$, instead of the circle $(D_1, A)$, we can draw the circle $(A, ED)$, where $E$ is the point diametrically opposite to the point $D_1$ of the circle $(A, B)$.

C o n s t r u c t i o n. (Second Method). We construct the segment $AC = nAB$ (Problem 2). We then describe the circles $(A, C)$, $(C, A)$ and $(C, AB)$ which intersect at the points $D$ and $E$. If we now describe the circles $(D, A)$ and $(C, DE)$ then at their intersection we obtain the point $X$. The segment $AX = \frac{1}{n} AB$ (Fig. 13).

P r o o f. The point $X$ lies on the straight line $AC$, since $AC$ is parallel to $DE$ and $XC$ is parallel to $DE$ (the

---

*For the definition of the angle of intersection of two curves, see Section 8, p. 71 below.

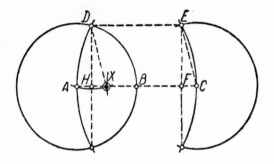

Fig. 13

figure *CEDX* is a parallelogram). From the similarity of the
isosceles triangles  *ACD*  and *AXD* we get

$$AX = \frac{1}{n} AB.$$

We now give the construction put forward by Smogorzhevskii*.
This construction differs from the preceding ones in that the
required $\frac{1}{n}$ th part of the segment *AB* does not lie on the given

segment.

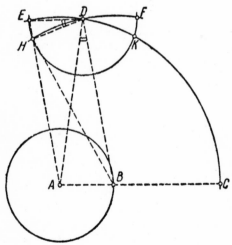

Fig. 14

*See bibliography, page  79 .

C o n s t r u c t i o n. (Third Method). We construct $AC = nAB$ (Problem 2). We draw the circles $(A, C)$ and $(B, AC)$ until they meet at the point $D$.

The circle $(D, AB)$ will intersect the two latter ones at the points $E$ and $H$. The segment $EH = \frac{1}{n} AB$ (Fig. 14).

P r o o f. From the congruence of triangles $ABD$, $ADE$ and $BDH$ (the three sides being equal), it follows that $\angle ADB = \angle EDH$. The isosceles triangles $ADB$ and $EDH$ are similar, consequently:

$$EH:ED = AB:AD$$

or

$$EH:AB = AB:nAB.$$

Finally

$$EH = \frac{1}{n} AB.$$

We shall note that

$$EK = \frac{\sqrt{n^2 - 1}}{n} AB,$$

$$HK = \left(2 - \frac{1}{n^2}\right) AB.$$

<u>Problem 10</u>. <u>To construct a segment equal to $\frac{1}{2^n}$ of a given segment $AB$ (divide the segment $AB$ into $2^n$ equal parts; $n = 2$, 3 ... ).</u>

C o n s t r u c t i o n. (First Method). We construct the segment $AC = 2 AB$ (Problem 2). We draw the circle $(C, A)$ and we denote by $D_1$ and $D_1'$ the points of its intersection with the circle $(A, B)$. If now we draw the circles $(D_1, A)$ and $(D_1', A)$ then at their intersection we obtain the point $X_1$. The segment $BX_1 = AX_1 = \frac{1}{2} AB$. We then describe the circle $(A, BD_1)$, and at the intersection with $(C, A)$ we obtain the point $D_2$ and $D_2'$. We draw the circles $(D_2, A)$ and $(D_2', A)$ until they meet at the point $X_2$. The segment $BX_2 = \frac{1}{2^2} AB$.

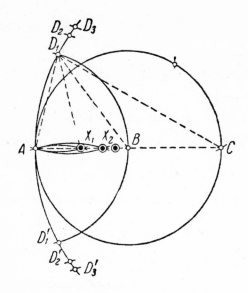

Fig. 15

If we further describe the circles $(A, BD_2)$ , $(D_2, A)$ and $(D_3', A)$ , then we get the point $X_3$. The segment $BX_3 = \frac{1}{2^3} AB$ and so on.

Proof. From the similarity of the isosceles triangles $ACD_1$ and $AD_1X_1$ it follows that

$$AD_1 : AC = AX_1 : AD_1$$

or

$$AB : 2\,AB = AX_1 : AB.$$

Hence

$$AX_1 = \frac{1}{2}\,AB.$$

We introduce the notation $AB = a$, $AD_k = m_k$, $k = 1, 2, 3, ..., n$ .

The segment $BD_1$ is the median of the triangle $ACD_1$, consequently

$$4\,BD_1^2 = 2\,AD_1^2 + 2\,CD_1^2 - AC^2$$

or, in another way,

$$4\,m_1^2 = 2\,AB^2 + 2\,AC^2 - AC^2 = 2\,AB^2 + AC^2 = 2\,AB^2 + 4AB^2.$$

This means that

$$m_1^2 = AD_1^2 = \frac{1+2}{2}\,a^2 = \frac{3}{2}\,a^2\,.$$

From the similarity of the isosceles triangles $ACD_2$ and $AD_2X_2$ we get

$$AD_2 : AC = AX_2 : AD_2$$

and taking into account that $AD_2 = BD_1 = m_1$ and $AC = 2a$ , we have

$$AX_2 = \frac{3}{4}\,a \quad \text{or} \quad BX_2 = \frac{1}{4}\,a = \frac{1}{2^2}\,AB.$$

Similarly we find

$$m_2^2 = \frac{1+2+2^2}{2^2}\,a^2 \text{ and } BX_3 = \frac{1}{2^3}\,AB,$$

and so on.  In general

$$m_{k-1}^2 = \frac{1+2+2^2+\ldots+2^{k-1}}{2^{k-1}}\,a^2 \text{ and } BX_k = \frac{1}{2^k}\,AB.$$

To divide the segment $AB$ into $2^n$ equal parts it is necessary to multiply the segment $AX_n, 2, 3, \ldots, 2^n$ times (Problem 2).

C o n s t r u c t i o n.  (Second Method).  We construct the segment $AC = 2AB$ (Problem 2), for which we draw the circle $(B, A)$ and we mark on it the chords $AE = EH = HC = a$ , we describe the circles $(A, C)$ and $(C, E)$ until their intersection at the points $D_1$ and $D_1'$ .

The required point $X_1$ is to be found at the intersection of the circles $(D_1, C)$ and $(D_1', C)$ .  The segment $BX_1 = \frac{1}{2}\,AB$ .

We describe the circle $(C, BD_1)$, intersecting $(A, C)$ at the points $D_2$ and $D_2'$ and then the circles $(D_2, BD_1)$ and $(D_2', BD_1)$ .  The latter ones, when intersecting, define the required point $X_2$ .  The segment $BX_2 = \frac{1}{2^2}\,AB$ (Fig. 16).  Similarly, describing the circles $(C, BD_2)$, $(D_3, BD_2)$ and $(D_3', BD_2)$ we construct the point $X_3$ .  The segment $BX_3 = \frac{1}{2^3}AB$  and so on.

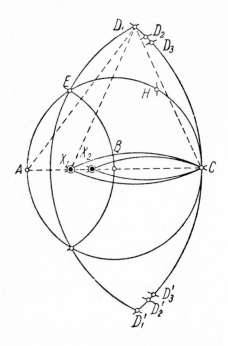

Fig. 16

P r o o f. From the similarity of the isosceles triangles $ACD_1$ and $CD_1X_1$ we get

$$CX_1:CD_1 = CD_1:AC.$$

Taking into account that $CD_1 = CE = \sqrt{3}\,AB$ we find: $CX_1 = \frac{3}{2}\,AB$, which means that $BX_1 = \frac{1}{2}\,AB$. Let us denote $BD_k = m_k$, where $k = 1, 2 \ldots, n$. The segment $BD_1$ is the median of the triangle $ACD_1$, consequently

$$4BD_1^2 = 4m_1^2 = 2AD_1^2 + 2CD_1^2 - AC^2 = 2AC^2 + 2CE^2 - AC^2 = 4a^2 + 2 \cdot 3a^2$$

or

$$m_1^2 = \left(1 + \frac{3}{2}\right) a^2 \ .$$

c

From the similarity of the triangles $ACD_2$ and $CD_2X_2$ we have

$$CX_2 : CD_2 = CD_2 : AC.$$

Noting that $CD_2 = BD_1 = m_1$ and $AC = 2AB = 2a$ we get

$$CX_2 = \frac{CD_2^2}{AC} = \frac{m_1^2}{2a} = \frac{5}{2^2} a .$$

It follows that

$$BX_2 = \frac{1}{2^2} AB .$$

In a completely similar way we shall prove that

$$m_2^2 = BD_2^2 = \frac{9}{4} a^2, \quad CX_3 = \frac{9}{8} a \quad \text{and} \quad BX_3 = \frac{1}{2^3} AB ,$$

etc.

In general

$$m_{k-1}^2 = BD_{k-1}^2 = \left( 1 + \frac{1}{2} + \frac{1}{2^2} + \cdots + \frac{1}{2^{k-2}} + \frac{3}{2^{k-1}} \right) a^2$$
$$\text{and } BX_k = \frac{1}{2^k} AB .$$

If, in the first method of construction, for large values of $k$ $(k \leqslant n)$ the point $X_k$ is not clearly defined (the arcs of the circles which define this point almost coincide with one another) then it is possible to solve the problem as follows:

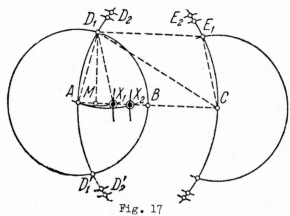

Fig. 17

C o n s t r u c t i o n.  (Third Method). We construct
the segment $AC = 2AB$ (Problem 2). We describe the circles
$(A, C)$, $(C, A)$ and $(C, AB)$. At their intersection we get the
point $D_1$ and $E_1$ (Fig. 17). At the intersection of the circles $(D_1, A)$ and $(C, D_1E_1)$ we obtain the required point $X_1$ .
The segment $BX_1 = \frac{1}{2} AB$ (Fig. 17). Furthermore, we construct
$AD_2 = CE_2 = BD_1$, towards which we describe the circles $(A, BD_1)$
and $(C, BD_1)$. We draw the circles $(D_2, A)$ and $(C, D_2E_2)$ until
they meet at the point $X_2$ . The segment $BX_2 = \frac{1}{2^2} AB$ , and
so on.

P r o o f.  The point $X_1$ lies on the straight line $AC$ ,
since $AC$ is parallel to $D_1E_1$ (the figure $AD_1E_1C$ is a trapezium)
and $X_1C$ is parallel to $D_1E_1$ (the figure $X_1D_1E_1C$ is a parallelogram), this means $X_1C$ is parallel to $AC$ . Similarly, it
can be established that the points $X_2, X_3, \ldots, X_n$ lie on the
straight line $AC$ .

From the preceding arguments it follows that $D_1X_1 = D_1'X_1$,
$D_2X_2 = D_2'X_2, \ldots$ . This means as was proved in the first method
of construction that $BX_1 = \frac{1}{2} AB$, $BX_2 = \frac{1}{2^2} AB$, $BX = \frac{1}{2^3} AB, \ldots$ .

Problem 11.  To construct a segment, $3^n$ times as great as
the given segment $AA_0$ $(n = 2, 3, \ldots)$ .

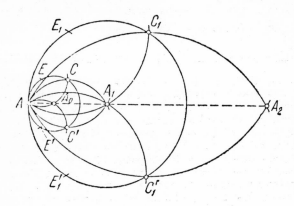

Fig. 18

C o n s t r u c t i o n. We describe the circle $(A_0, A)$ and, without changing the opening of the compasses, we measure off the chords $AE = EC$, $AE' = E'C'$. We draw the circles $(C, A)$ and $(C', A)$ until they intersect at the point $A_1$. The segment $AA_1 = 3AA_0$ (Fig. 18).

We then draw the circles $(A_1, A)$ and we measure off the chords $AE_1 = E_1C_1$, $AE'_1 = E'_1C'_1$. At the intersection of the circles $(C_1, A)$ and $(C'_1, A)$ we obtain the point $A_2$. The segment $AA_2 = 3^2 AA_0$ and so on. The validity of the construction is self-evident.

Problem 12. <u>To divide the segment $AB$ into three equal parts</u>. Let us examine an elegant method of construction put forward by Mascheroni.

C o n s t r u c t i o n. We construct $AC = AB = BD$ (Problem 2). We describe the circles $(C, B)$, $(C, D)$, $(D, A)$ and $(D, C)$, at whose intersections we obtain the points $E$, $E_1$, $F$ and $F_1$. The circles $(E, C)$ and $(E_1, C)$, $(F, D)$ and $(F_1, D)$ define the required points $X$ and $Y$, which divide the segment $AB$ into three equal parts (Fig. 19).

P r o o f. It follows from the similarity of the isosceles triangles $CEX$ and $CDE$ that

$$CX : CE = CE : DC.$$

Taking into account that $CE = 2AB$ and $CD = 3AB$, we obtain $CX = \frac{4}{3} AB$, therefore $AX = \frac{1}{3} AB$.

Problem 13. <u>Construct the centre of a given circle.</u>

C o n s t r u c t i o n. On the circumference of the given circle we take a point $A$, and with an arbitrary radius $d$ we describe the circle $(A, d)$. At the intersection (with the original circle) we obtain the points $B$ and $D$. On the circumference of $(A, d)$ we construct the point $C$ diametrically opposite to $B$. We further draw the circles $(C, D)$ and $(A, CD)$; we denote by $E$ their point of intersection. Finally, we describe the circle $(E, CD)$ to meet $(A, d)$ at the point $M$. The point $BM$ equals the radius of the given circle. The circles $(B, M)$ and $(A, BM)$ define the required centre of the given circle (Fig. 20).

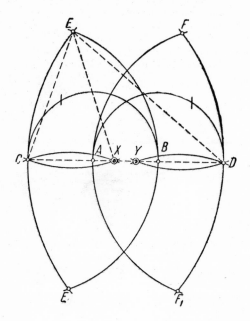

Fig. 19

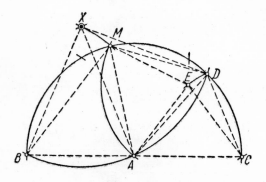

Fig. 20

P r o o f. The isosceles triangles $ACE$ and $AEM$ are equal, therefore $\angle EAM = \angle ACE$.

On the one hand, $\angle BAE = \angle ACE + \angle AEC$ ($\angle BAE$ is an exterior angle of the triangle $ACE$) on the other hand, $\angle BAE = \angle BAM + \angle EAM$.

Hence

$$\angle BAM = \angle AEC.$$

Thus, the isosceles triangles $ABM$ and $ACE$ are similar, therefore

$$BM : AB = AC : CE$$

or

$$BX : AB = AC : CD.$$

From the latter proportion it follows that the isosceles triangles $ABX$ and $ACD$ are similar, which means that

$$\angle BAX = \angle ACD = \tfrac{1}{2} \angle BAD = \angle DAX;$$

the latter two equations follow from

$$\angle BAD = \angle ADC + \angle ACD = 2 \angle ACD = 2 \angle BAX.$$

On the basis of the equality of the angles $BAX$ and $DAX$ we conclude that the isosceles triangles $ABX$ and $ADX$ are equal, therefore

$$BX = AX = DX.$$

The point $X$ is the required centre of the circle.

N o t e. We should make the segment $d = AB$ greater than half the radius of the given circle, otherwise the circles $(C, D)$ and $(A, CD)$ will not intersect.

To conclude this chapter we give without proof the solution of the following problem of Mascheroni [10].

Problem 14. Construct the segment $\tfrac{1}{2} \sqrt{n}\, AB$, where $AB = 1$, $n = 1, \ldots, 25$.

C o n s t r u c t i o n. We describe the circle $(A, B)$ and, with radius $AB$, which, for the sake of simplicity of notation, is taken to be a unit segment, we measure off the chords

$BC = CD = DE$ . We draw the circles $(B, D)$ and $(E, C)$ until they meet at the points $F$ and $F_1$ . We describe the circles $(B, AF)$ and $(E, AF)$ which intersect $(A, B)$ at the points $H$ and $H_1$ , and the circles $(B, D)$ and $(E, C)$ at the points $N, N_1, M$ and $M_1$ . We describe the circles $(E, A)$ and $(B, A)$ and we mark the points $P, P_1, Q$ and $Q_1$ of their intersection with the circles $(B, AF)$ and $(E, AF)$ . The circles $(P, B)$ and $(P_1, B)$ will intersect at the point $R$ and they will intersect the circle $(A, B)$ at the points $S$ and $S_1$ . Exactly in the same way, the circles $(Q, E)$ and $(Q_1, E)$ will intersect at the point $T$ and they will intersect the circle $(A, B)$ at the points $O$ and $O_1$ . We draw

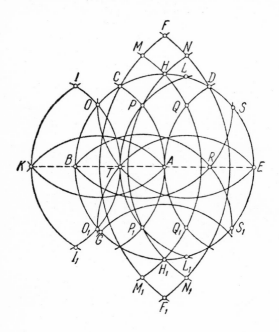

Fig. 21

the circles $(R, AB)$ and $(F_1, AB)$ until they meet the circle $(A, B)$ at the points $L, L_1$ and $G$ . The circles $(O, A)$ and $(O_1, A)$ intersect and so define the point $K$ . Finally, we draw the circles $(K, AB)$ and $(T, AB)$ which, intersecting, give the points $I$ and $I_1$ . Then

$$AT = \frac{1}{2}\sqrt{1}, \quad QQ_1 = \frac{1}{2}\sqrt{7}, \quad HK = \frac{1}{2}\sqrt{13}, \quad KD = \frac{1}{2}\sqrt{19},$$
$$PT = \frac{1}{2}\sqrt{2}, \quad AF = \frac{1}{2}\sqrt{8}, \quad BS = \frac{1}{2}\sqrt{14}, \quad FG = \frac{1}{2}\sqrt{20},$$
$$DR = \frac{1}{2}\sqrt{3}, \quad BR = \frac{1}{2}\sqrt{9}, \quad LL_1 = \frac{1}{2}\sqrt{15}, \quad I_1D = \frac{1}{2}\sqrt{21},$$
$$AB = \frac{1}{2}\sqrt{4}, \quad BL = \frac{1}{2}\sqrt{10}, \quad BE = \frac{1}{2}\sqrt{16}, \quad KS = \frac{1}{2}\sqrt{22},$$
$$HT = \frac{1}{2}\sqrt{5}, \quad PS_1 = \frac{1}{2}\sqrt{11}, \quad FK = \frac{1}{2}\sqrt{17}, \quad MM_1 = \frac{1}{2}\sqrt{23},$$
$$AM = \frac{1}{2}\sqrt{6}, \quad BD = \frac{1}{2}\sqrt{12}, \quad KN = \frac{1}{2}\sqrt{18}, \quad MN_1 = \frac{1}{2}\sqrt{24},$$
$$KE = \frac{1}{2}\sqrt{25} = \frac{1}{2}\sqrt{25} \, AB.$$

## 3. INVERSION AND ITS PRINCIPAL PROPERTIES

At the end of the 19th century, Adler applied the principle of inversion to the theory of geometrical constructions with compasses alone. With the help of this principle he established a general method of solving construction problems in the geometry of compasses.

In this section we shall give the definition of inversion and we shall dwell briefly on its principal properties, which will be made use of in our further discussions.

In the plane of the drawing, let a circle $(O, r)$ be given, also a point $P$ other than $O$.

On the ray $OP$, take a point $P'$ in such a way that the product of the segments $OP$ and $OP'$ are equal to the square of the radius of the given circle, i.e.

$$OP \cdot OP' = r^2; \tag{1}$$

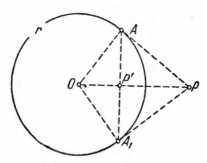

Fig. 22

Such a point $P'$ is called the inverse of the point $P$ with respect to the circle $(O, r)$. The circle $(O, r)$ is called the circle of inversion, its centre is called the centre of inversion or the pole of inversion and the quantity $r^2$ is called the power of inversion.

If the point $P'$ is inverse of the point $P$ , then, obviously, the point $P$ is inverse of the point $P'$ .

The correspondence between inverse points, or, in other words, the transformation, which associates with each point $P$ of some figure the corresponding inverse point $P'$ , is called inversion*. From the definition of inversion it follows that to each point $P$ in the plane there corresponds a definite and unique point $P'$ in the same plane, and if $OP > r$, $OP' < r$ . The exception is the centre $O$ of the circle of inversion. No point in the plane can be inverse of $O$ , which follows immediately from equation (1)**.

Let $AP$ and $A_1P$ be tangents to the circle of inversion $(O, r)$ drawn from the point $P$ outside of this circle (Fig. 22). Then the point of intersection $P'$ of the straight lines $AA_1$ and $OP$ is the inverse of the point $P$. Indeed, in the right-angled triangle $OAP$ $(AP'$ is the height)

$$OP \cdot OP' = OA^2 = r^2.$$

If the point $P$ moves along some curve $l$ then its inverse point $P'$ will also describe some curve $l'$ . The curves $l$ and $l'$ are called mutually inverse.

L e m m a. If the points $P'$ and $Q'$ are the inverse points of the points $P$ and $Q$ with respect to the circle $(O, r)$ , then

---

*Let us put $OA = r = 1, OP = R, OP' = R'$, equation (1) in this case can be written as $R = \dfrac{1}{R'}$ . The distances of the inverse points $P$ and $P'$ from the centre of inversion $O$ are reciprocal numbers. Inversion (Latin inversio) literally means turning over, changing places.

**In Higher Geometry certain considerations lead to regard 'an infinitely distant' point in the plane as corresponding to the centre $O$ . When the point $P'$ approaches the centre of inversion $O$ , the segment $OP'$ decreases. Then, in order that equation (1) should remain valid, the segment $OP$ must increase and $P$ will move further and further away from the centre of inversion $O$ , i.e. if $OP' \to 0$ then $OP \to \infty$ .

$$\measuredangle \, OP'Q' = \measuredangle \, OQP, \ \measuredangle \, OQ'P' = \measuredangle \, OPQ.$$

P r o o f .  From the equations $OP \cdot OP' = OQ \cdot OQ' = r^2$ or $\dfrac{OP}{OQ} = \dfrac{OQ'}{OP'}$ it follows that the triangles $OQ'P'$ and $OQP$ are similar (Fig. 23). This proves the lemma. From the definition of

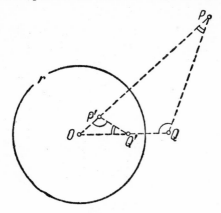

Fig. 23

inversion three theorems follow immediately:

T h e o r e m  1. <u>If two curves intersect at the point</u> <u>$P$ , then their inverse curves intersect at a point $P'$ which</u> <u>is the inverse of the point $P$ .</u>

T h e o r e m  2. <u>A straight line passing through the</u> <u>centre of inversion $O$ is its own inverse.</u>

T h e o r e m  3. <u>The curve which is inverse to a given</u> <u>straight line $AB$, not passing through the centre of inver-</u> <u>sion, is the circle $(O_1, \, OO_1)$ , which passes through the centre</u> <u>of inversion $O \cdot$, and $OO_1$ is perpendicular to $AB$ .</u>

P r o o f .  Let $Q$ be the foot of the perpendicular drawn from the centre of inversion $O$ to the given straight line. Let us denote the point  inverse of the point $Q$ by  $Q'$ . Let us take an arbitrary point $P$ on the given straight line and let us denote its inverse point by  $P'$   (Fig. 24).

On the basis of the lemma we can write

$$\measuredangle\ OP'Q' = \measuredangle\ OQP = 90°.$$

Consequently, when the point $P$ moves along the straight line $AB$ ; its inverse $P'$ describes a circle with the segment $OQ'$ as its diameter.

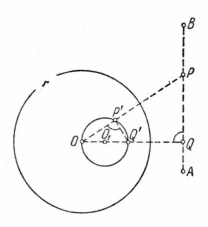

Fig. 24

As the circle $(O_1,\ OO_1)$ and the given straight line $AB$ are mutually inverse, then the converse proposition also holds.

T h e o r e m    4. <u>The inverse of the given circle $(O_1, R)$ , not passing through the centre of inversion, is also a circle. Further, the centre of inversion is the centre of similitude of these circles.</u>

P r o o f.  Let the line $OO_1$ joining the centres of the circle of inversion $(O,\ r)$ and the given circle $(O_1,\ R)$  intersect the latter at the points $A$ and $B$ . Let us denote by $A'$ and $B'$ inverse points of the points $A$ and $B$ . Let us take an arbitrary point $P$ on the circle $(O_1,\ R)$ and let us denote its inverse by $P'$ (Fig. 25).  Applying the lemma, we obtain:

$$\measuredangle\ OA'P = \measuredangle\ OPA \ \text{ and } \measuredangle\ OB'P = \measuredangle\ OPB,$$

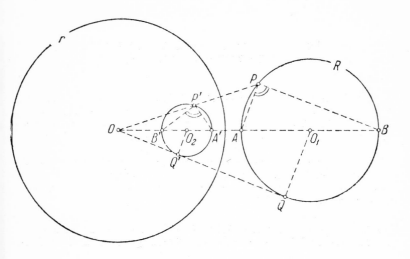

Fig. 25

Hence

$$\measuredangle\, OB'P' - \measuredangle\, OA'P' = \measuredangle\, OPB - \measuredangle\, OPA.$$

In the triangles  $A'B'P'$  and  $ABP$

$$\measuredangle\, A'P'B' = \measuredangle\, OB'P' - \measuredangle\, OA'P' \text{ and } \measuredangle\, APB =$$
$$= \measuredangle\, OPB - \measuredangle\, OPA = 90°.$$

Taking into account the preceding equation we get

$$\measuredangle\, A'P'B' = \measuredangle\, APB = 90°.$$

Now, let the point $P$ describe the given circle  $(O_1, R)$  ; then its inverse,  $P'$  , will describe the circle  $(O_2,\ P')$  , which has the segment $A'B'$ as its diameter. The theorem has thus been proved.

If $QQ'$ is the common outer tangent of the given circle $(O_1,\ R)$ and the inverse circle $(O_2,\ P')$ then the points of contact $Q$ and $Q'$ are always inverses of each other. The perpendicular at the point $Q$ to the tangent $QQ'$, intersects the line of centres $OO_1$ at the point  $O_2$ , the centre of the circle inverse to the given one.

## 4. THE APPLICATION OF THE METHOD OF INVERSION
## TO THE GEOMETRY OF COMPASSES

The application of the method of inversion to the solution of geometrical construction problems by means of compasses alone  yields a general approach to the solution of construction problems in the geometry of compasses.

The constructions of Mohr and Mascheroni, although extremely elegant, nevertheless are  in most cases obtained by such artificial means  that the question arises how each of these constructions was established.

Problem 15. To construct the point $X$, inverse of the given point $C$ with respect to the circle of inversion $(O, r)$ .

C o n s t r u c t i o n. In the case of  $OC > \frac{r}{2}$ (Fig. 26). We draw the circle $(C ,O)$ to meet the circle of inversion at the points $D$ and $D_1$ . If, now, the circles $(D, O)$ and $(D_1, O)$ are drawn, then at the intersection we obtain the required point $X$ .

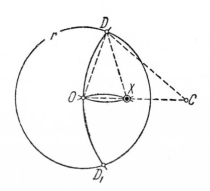

Fig. 26

P r o o f. From the similarity of the isosceles triangles

$CDO$ and $DOX$ we find

$$OC:OD = OD:OX$$

or

$$OC \cdot OX = OD^2 = r^2$$

N o t e .  It is easy to see that the above construction coincides with the solution of Problem 9 (First Method) when the segment $AC = nAB$ is not constructed, but the point $C$ is regarded as already given. Thus, the second method of solving Problem 9 can be used also in the construction of the inverse point $X$ of the given point $C$; here the point $C$ is given, and the construction of the segment $AC = nAB$ should not be carried out. Construction in the case $OC \leqslant \frac{r}{2}$ (Fig. 27). The circle $(C, O)$ will not intersect the circle of inversion, therefore we construct first the segment $OC_1 = nOC$, taking such a natural number $n$, that $OC_1 > \frac{r}{2}$ (Problem 2). We find the inverse point, $C_1'$, of $C_1$ (First method of construction of the problem under discussion). We construct the segment $OX = nOC_1'$. The point $X$ is inverse of the given point $C$.

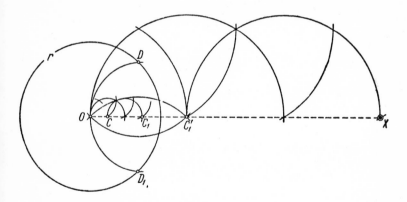

Fig. 27

P r o o f .  Substituting $OC_1 = nOC$ and $OC_1' = \frac{OX}{n}$ in the equation $OC_1 \cdot OC_1' = r^2$, we get

$$OC_1 \cdot OC_1' = nOC \cdot \frac{OX}{n} = OC \cdot OX = r^2.$$

Problem 16. Given the circle of inversion $(O, r)$ and the
straight line $AB$, which does not pass through the centre of
inversion, construct the circle which is the inverse of the
given straight line.

C o n s t r u c t i o n. We construct $O_1$, symmetrical
to the centre of inversion $O$, with respect to the straight
line $AB$ (Problem 1). We find the point $O_1'$, inverse of the
point $O_1$ (Problem 15). The circle $(O_1', O)$ is inverse of the
given straight line $AB$ (Fig. 28).

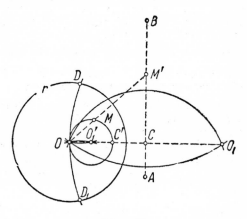

Fig. 28

P r o o f. Let $C$ and $C'$ be the points of intersection of
the straight line $OO_1$ with the given straight line $AB$ and
the circle $(O_1', O)$ .

It follows from the above construction that

$$OO_1 \cdot OO_1' = r^2, \ OO_1 = 2OC, \ OC' = 2OO_1', \ OC \perp AB.$$

Hence

$$OO_1 \cdot OO_1' = 2OC \cdot \frac{OC'}{2} = OC \cdot OC' = r^2.$$

According to Theorem 3, the circle $(O_1', \ O)$ is the inverse of
the straight line $AB$ .

Problem 17. To construct the straight line $AB$, which is
the inverse of the given circle $(O_1, R)$ passing through the

centre of inversion  $O$.

Construction. If the given circle intersects
the circle of inversion at the points $A$ and $B$ , then the
straight line $AB$ is the inverse of this circle. Otherwise,
we take the points $A_1$ and $B_1$ (Fig. 29) on the given circle,
and we construct their inverses, $A$ and $B$ (Problem 15). The
straight line $AB$ is the inverse of the given circle $(O_1, R)$ .
By varying the position of the points $A_1$ and $B_1$ on the given
circle, it is possible to construct as many points of this
straight line as required. The validity of this construction
is self-evident (see Theorem 3).

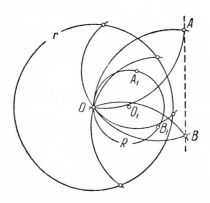

Fig. 29

Problem 18. A given circle $(O_1, R)$ does not pass through
the centre of inversion  $O$.  Construct the circle which is
inverse of the given one.

Construction. We take the given circle $(O_1, R)$
as the circle of inversion and we construct the inverse point
$O'$ of the point $O$ (Problem 15). Then we construct the inverse point $O_2$ of the point $O'$ with respect to the circle of
inversion $(O, r)$ . The point $O_2$ is the centre of the circle
required (Fig. 30).

We take any point $A$ on the given circle $(O_1, R)$ and we find
the inverse  $A'$ . The circle $(O_2, A')$ is inverse of the given
circle $(O_1, R)$.

D

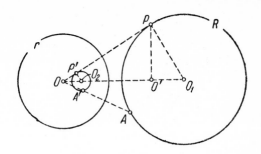

Fig. 30

P r o o f . Let $PP'$ be the direct common tangent of the circles $(O_1, R)$ and $(O_2, A')$ and let $PO'$ be perpendicular to $OO_1$ .

From the similarity of the triangles $OPO'$ and $OP'O_2$ we have

$$OO_2 : OP' = OP : OO'$$

or, alternatively

$$OO_2 \cdot OO' = OP \cdot OP' = r^2,$$

since the points $P$ and $P'$ are inverse. It follows from the last equation that the points $O_2$ and $O'$ are inverse with respect to the circle of inversion $(O, r)$ .

In the right-angled triangle $OO_1P$ , the segment $O'P$ is the altitude, therefore,

$$O_1O \cdot O_1O' = (\overline{O_1P})^2 = R^2.$$

Thus, the point $O'$ is the inverse of the point $O$ with respect to the circle $(O_1, R)$ if the latter is taken as the circle of inversion.

The point $O$ is given. In construction, the point $O'$ was found first, then the point $O_2$ , the centre of the required circle, was found.

In Problems 15-18 it was shown  how to construct figures
to find the inverse of a point, a straight line and a circle,
using compasses alone. We now examine a general method of
solving geometrical construction problems with compasses alone.

Each construction carried out by means of compasses and a
ruler gives a figure Φ in the plane of the drawing, consisting of separate points, straight lines and circles. The inverse figure  Φ′ of the figure Φ with respect to the circle
(O, r) , which is taken as the circle of inversion, with the
centre O  not lying on any of the straight lines and circles
of figure Φ , consists only of points and circles.

Using Problems 15-18, we see that each of these points and
straight lines can be constructed by compasses alone.

Now, let a certain construction problem, soluble by means of
a ruler and compasses, be required to be solved by means of
compasses alone.

Let us imagine that this problem has been solved by means
of compasses and a ruler, as a result of which a certain figure Φ has been obtained, consisting of points, straight lines
and circles. The construction of this figure was realized
by carrying out a finite number of constructions of straight
lines and circles in a definite order.

Let us take the most suitable circle of inversion (O, r) and
let us construct the figure  Φ′ , inverse of the figure  Φ
(Problems 15-18). The figure Φ′ will consist of points and
circles only, if, of course, the circle of inversion has been
chosen such, that its centre does not lie on any of the
straight lines or circles of figure Φ.

If we now construct the inverse of the figure which is taken
as the result in the figure Φ′, then we arrive at the required
result.

We should note here that we should carry out the construction of figure Φ′ in the order  in which the construction of
figure Φ was carried out by means of compasses and a ruler.

By means of the method described above it is possible to
solve by compasses alone each construction problem  soluble
by means of compasses and a ruler. The basic Mohr-Mascheroni
result has been proved once again, this time with the help
of the method of inversion.

The five simplest problems mentioned at the end of Section

1 can also be solved by the general method.

We take the solution of Problem 7 as an illustration of the general method of solving construction problems. We shall construct the point of intersection of two straight lines $AB$ and $CD$ , each of which is given by two points.

We take an arbitrary circle $(O, r)$ in the plane, with centre $O$ , not on any of the given straight lines, and we regard it as the circle of inversion. We construct the circles which are the inverses of the given straight lines and we mark their point of intersection $X'$ (Problem 16). We construct the point $X$ inverse of the point $X'$ (Problem 15). $X$ is the required point of intersection of the given straight lines $AB$ and $CD$ .

Here the figure $\Phi$ consists of two given straight lines $AB$ and $CD$ (more exactly, it consists of 4 given points $A$, $B$, $C$ and $D$ , through which we mentally draw the given lines); the figure $\Phi'$ consists of two circles, inverses of the given straight lines $AB$ and $CD$ . The image taken as the result in figure $\Phi'$ will be the point $X'$ . The point $X$ inverse of the point $X'$ is the required result, the point of the intersection of the given straight lines.

Exactly in the same way, it is possible to solve Problem 6 (the fourth of the simplest problems) - to construct the points of intersection of a given straight line and a given circle. The solution of the problem will be considerably simplified at the same time. The truth of these constructions follows immediately from Theorem 1.

### Problem 19. To find the centre of a given circle.

C o n s t r u c t i o n. We take a point $O$ on the given circle, and with an arbitrary radius $r$ we describe a circle $(O, r)$ which intersects the given circle at the points $A$ and $B$ . We take the circle $(O, r)$ as the circle of inversion and we construct the centre of the circle which is the inverse of the straight line $AB$ (Problem 16). In order to carry out the latter construction, we draw the circles $(A, O)$ and $(B, O)$ until they meet at the point $O_1$ , we describe the circle $(O_1, O)$ and we mark the points $D$ and $D_1$ of its intersection with the circle of inversion. The circles $(D, O)$ and $(D_1, O)$ define the required centre of the original circle (Fig. 31).

P r o o f. The points A and B are inverses of each other, since they lie on the circle of inversion. Thus, the given circle and the straight line AB are mutually inverse figures.

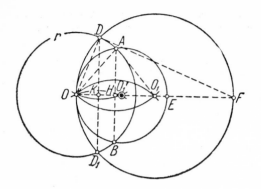

Fig. 31

In Problem 16 it was shown that the point $O_1'$ was the required centre of the given circle, which, in this case, is the inverse of the straight line AB .

The attention of the reader should be drawn to the simplicity and elegance of the solution of the last problem.

In order to find the centre of the circle, six circles have been drawn*. This construction is simpler and more exact than the more usual construction with a ruler and compasses.

This problem, and also certain other problems in the geometry of compasses, as, for example, Problems 3 and 8 (Second Method) can be given to older pupils as exercises during geometry lessons. For this reason, we give a proof of the construction in Problem 19, which is not based on the principle of inversion.

P r o o f. The straight line $OO_1$ is perpendicular to the chord AB of the given circle and passes through its midpoint,

*Of course, on condition that the radius r is made greater than half of the radius of the given circle. Otherwise, there will be a greater number of circles (see the solution of Problem 15 - case 2).

therefore the required centre must lie on the straight line $OO_1$ . Let $E$ and $F$ be the points of intersection of the straight line $OO_1$ with the given circle and with the circle $(O_1, O)$. The segment $OE$ is the diameter of the given circle.

Examining the right-angled triangles $OAE$ and $ODF$ , whose altitudes are the segments $AH$ and $DK$ , we find

$$OA^2 = OE \cdot OH \text{ and } OD^2 = OF \cdot OK.$$

Taking into account that $OD = OA = r$, $OF = 2OO_1$, $OH = \frac{1}{2} OO_1$ and $OK = \frac{1}{2} OO_1'$ , we obtain

$$OE \cdot OH = OF \cdot OK$$

or

$$OE \cdot \frac{OO_1}{2} = 2 \cdot OO_1 \cdot \frac{OO_1'}{2} .$$

Hence

$$OO_1' = \frac{OE}{2} .$$

Problem 20. Circumscribe a circle round a given triangle $ABC$ .

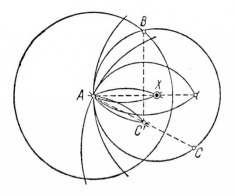

Fig. 32

C o n s t r u c t i o n. We describe the circle $(A, B)$ and take it as the circle of inversion. We construct the inverse point $C'$ of the point $C$ (Problem 15). We construct the circle $(X, A)$, which is the inverse of the straight line $BC'$ (Problem 16). $(X, A)$ is the required circle, circumscribed round the triangle $ABC$.

P r o o f. The point $B$ is its own inverse since it lies on the circle of inversion $(A, B)$ . The point $C'$ is the inverse of the point $C$ . It follows that the circle passing through the given points $A$, $B$ and $C$ is the inverse of the straight line $BC'$ . And, as was shown in Problem 16, the point $X$ is the centre of the required circle*.

N o t e. We can now give the following method of solving Problem 18. We take arbitrary points $A$, $B$ and $C$ on the given circle $(O_1, R)$ and we construct their inverses, $A'$, $B'$ and $C'$ . The circle, circumscribed round the triangle $A'B'C'$, is the required inverse of the given circle.

---

*In Problem 16 we constructed the centre of a circle, which is inverse of a given straight line. This construction was used in solving Problems 19 and 20.

# Part 2

# Geometric constructions by means of compasses alone but with restrictions

In Part One of this book we investigated constructions by means of compasses alone which we can now call the classical geometry of compasses.

In the theory of geometric constructions by means of compasses alone, the free use of the compasses is always understood; no restrictions are put on the size of the angle made by the legs.

With such compasses it is possible to draw circles with radii as large or as small as we please.

It is well known, however, that in practice, with actual compasses, it is possible to describe circles, whose radii are no larger than a certain length $R_{max}$ and no smaller than a length $R_{min}$. The length $R_{max}$ corresponds to the maximal, and $R_{min}$ to the minimal opening of the legs of the given compasses. If we denote by $r$ the radius of a circle, which can be described with these compasses, the following inequality always holds:

$$R_{min} \leqslant r \leqslant R_{max}.$$

We shall say that in this case the opening of the legs of the compasses is restricted from below by the length $R_{min}$, and restricted from above by the length $R_{max}$.

In Part Two we shall examine geometrical constructions by means of compasses alone, when certain restrictions are imposed on the opening of the legs.

## 5. CONSTRUCTIONS BY MEANS OF COMPASSES ALONE WITH THE OPENING OF THE LEGS RESTRICTED FROM ABOVE

In this chapter we shall use compasses the opening of whose legs is restricted, from above only, by the given length $R_{max}$ . With such compasses it is possible to describe circles whose radii do not exceed this length. For the sake of brevity, we shall henceforward write simply $R$, instead of $R_{max}$ .

If we denote the radius of a circle, which it is possible to draw with these compasses, by $r$ , then we always have

$$O < r \leqslant R.$$

Problem 21. To construct a segment, which is $\frac{1}{2^n}$ th part of a given segment $AB$ (to divide the given segment $AB$ into 2, 4, 8, ..., $2^n$ equal parts).

It is not hard to verify that in the case when $AB \leqslant \frac{R}{2}$ *
it is possible to use the construction contained in Problem 10; the radius of the greatest circle in that construction is equal to $AC = 2AB < R$ ** .

---

*To compare two given segments $AB$ and $CD$ , one should describe the circle $(A, CD)$; if the point $B$ lies (a) inside this circle, then $AB < CD$, (b) on the circumference, then $AB = CD$, (c) outside the circle, then $AB > CD$ .

To verify the inequality $AB \leqslant \frac{1}{2} R$ or the inequality $R \geqslant 2AB$ , the circle $(A, R)$ has to be drawn; if the point $B$ lies on the circumference $(A, R)$ or outside of it, then $R < 2AB$ ; if the point $B$ lies inside the circle, then $AB < R$ , and, therefore, the segment $2AB$ can be constructed (Problem 2), and compared with the segment $R$ by the means indicated above.
**In the first method of construction of Problem 10, it is necessary to check that $AD_n \leqslant R$ for all $n = 1, 2, 3, ...$

47

C o n s t r u c t i o n  in the case of $AB < 2R$ *. With an arbitrary radius $r$ we describe the circles $(A, r)$ and $(B, r)$ and we denote their points of intersection by $C$ and $D$. Varying the size of the radius $r$, it is always possible to get $CD$ to be less than or equal to $\frac{R}{2}$. Now we bisect the segment $CD$ (Problem 10). We obtain a point $X_1$. Obviously, the point $X_1$ bisects the given segment $AB$ also.

Exactly in the same way we construct the point $X_2$, bisecting the segment $AX_1$. The segment $AX_2 = \frac{1}{4} AB \leqslant \frac{R}{2}$. The construction of points $X_3, X_4, \ldots, X_n$ can be reduced to solving Problem 10.

If we increase $BX_n = \frac{AB}{2^n} 2^n$ times (Problem 2) we will have divided the segment $AB$ into $2^n$ equal parts.

Problem 22. (The first basic operation). To construct one or several points on the straight line given by two points $A$ and $B$ **.

C o n s t r u c t i o n  in the case when $AB < 2R$, is reducible to Problem 5.

C o n s t r u c t i o n  in the case when $AB \geqslant 2R$. We describe the circles $(B, R)$ and $(A, r)$, where $r$ is an arbitrary length, smaller than or equal to $R$. We take a point on the circumference of the circle $(A, r)$, such that it should lie 'approximately' on the segment $AB$ (i.e. such that the angle $CAB$ is as small as possible), and we construct the segment

$$\lim_{n \to \infty} \overline{AD}_n^2 = \lim_{n \to \infty} \left(1 + \frac{1}{2} + \frac{1}{2^2} + \ldots + \frac{1}{2^n}\right) a^2 =$$
$$= \left(1 + \frac{1}{2} + \frac{1}{2^2} + \ldots + \frac{1}{2^n} + \ldots\right) a^2 = \frac{a^2}{1 - \frac{1}{2}} = 2a^2 = 2AB^2,$$

i.e. $AD_n < \sqrt{2} AB < R$.
*If the circles $(A, R)$ and $(B, R)$ do not intersect, then $AB > 2R$.
**As we have already remarked, we cannot draw a continuous straight line with compasses alone, still less with compasses the opening of whose legs is restricted. However, we shall be able to construct any number of points of this straight line.

$AD = mAC$ (Problem 2, $AC = r \leqslant R$ . We pick the natural number $m$ so that the point $D$ lies inside the circle $(B, R)$*.

Varying the position of the point $C$ on the arc $(A, r)$ , and,
if necessary, varying the size of the radius $r$ , it is always
possible to get the point $D$ to lie inside the circle $(B, R)$ .
At the same time we construct the segments $AC = \ldots = HD = \dfrac{AD}{m}$
(Fig. 33).

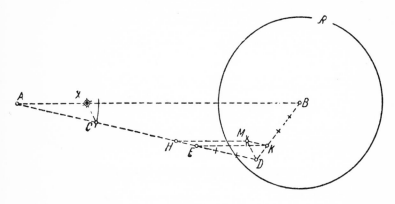

Fig. 33

Let us take a natural number $n$ such that $2^{n-1} < m \leqslant 2^n$ . We
construct the segment $DK = \dfrac{1}{2^n} BD$ (Problem 21, here $BD < 2R$).
We divide the segment $DH$ into $2^n$ equal parts (Problem 21,
$DH = r \leqslant R$) and we take a segment $DE = \dfrac{m}{2^n} DH$ (in Fig. 33,
$m = 3$, $2^{2-1} < 3 < 2^2$, $n = 2$, $DE = \dfrac{3}{4} DH$).

We construct the parallelogram $HEKM$. To do this, it is
necessary to draw the circles $(H, EK)$ and $(K, EH)$ . (If, at the
intersection of these circles, the point $M$ is not clearly
defined, then, in order to construct the point $M$, we should
draw the circle $(E, K)$ and mark off on it the chords $KP = PT$ ,

---

*The point $D$ does not need to lie inside the circle $(B, R)$;
it is important  that $BD$ should be less than $2R$ . The point
should lie in the circle $(B, 2R)$ but we cannot describe such a
circle with the given compasses.

equal to the radius $EK$ . At the intersection of the circles $(H, EK)$ and $(P, TH)$ we get the point $M$ .)

Finally, when we draw the circles $(A, HM)$ and $(C, DM)$ , they will intersect at the required point $X$ , lying on the straight line $AB$ .

Further construction of points of the given straight line $AB$ comes down to Problem $(AX \leqslant R)$ .

P r o o f. From the construction we have

$$\frac{BD}{DK} = 2^n \text{ and } \frac{AD}{DE} = \frac{m\,AC}{\frac{m}{2^n}\,AC} = 2^n.$$

Thus the triangles $ADB$ and $DEK$ are similar (the angle $ADB$ is a common one). This means that

$$\angle DEK = \angle DAB \text{ and } EK \parallel AB.$$

As $HM$ is parallel to $EK$ (the figure $HEKM$ is a parallelogram), therefore $HM$ is parallel to $AB$ . From the congruence of the triangles $ACX$ and $DHM$ it follows that $AX$ is parallel to $HM$ , i.e. the point $X$ lies on the straight line $AB$ .

None of the radii of the circles drawn in this construction exceed the segment $R$ .

N o t e. If it turns out that $m = 2^n$, i.e. if $m$ takes one of the values 2, 4, 8, 16, ..., the construction of this problem is considerably simplified. In this case, the point $E$ coincides with point $H$, and the point $M$ coincides with the point $K$ . The dividing of the segment $DH$ into $2^n$ equal parts and the construction of the parallelogram $EKMH$ is dispensed with in this case.

Thus, while varying the size of radius $r$ , we should always try to make the number $m$ take one of the values 2, 4, 8, 16, ... $n$.

Problem 23. To mark off from the point $C$ to the right (or to the left) a segment  parallel and equal to a given segment $AB$ .

If the point $C$ does not lie on the straight line $AB$ , the problem is reduced to the construction of the parallelogram $ABDC$ (or $ABCD'$ ).

C o n s t r u c t i o n  in the case when $AB \leqslant R$ . Let
$AC \leqslant R$  and suppose that the point $C$  does not lie on the
straight line  $AB$ .  We describe the circles $(C, AB)$ and $(B, AC)$
and we mark the point of their intersection $D$ .  The segment $CD$ is the required one.  The figure $ABDC$ is a parallelogram.

If it is necessary to measure off the segment from the
point $C$  in the opposite direction, then we have to draw the
circle $(A, BC)$ instead of the circle  $(B, AC)$ .  In the case
$BC > R$ we cannot describe the circle $(A, BC)$  with the given
compasses.  We can obtain the required point, however, if
we construct on the circumference of the circle $(C, AB)$ the
point $D'$ , diametrically opposite to $D$ .  The figure  $ABD'C$
is the required parallelogram.

Now, let $AC > R$ and $BC > R$  (Fig. 34).  We take an arbitrary
row of points  $A_1, A_2, ..., A_k$ in the direction from point  $A$

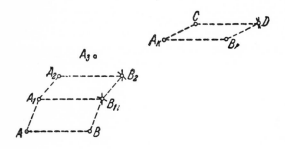

Fig. 34

towards point  $C$ , satisfying $AA_1 \leqslant R,\ A_1A_2 \leqslant R, ..., A_kC \leqslant R,$ and
we construct the parallelograms $ABB_1A_1,\ A_1B_1B_2A_2, ...,\ A_{k-1}$
$B_{k-1}B_kA_k$ .    Then we construct the parallelogram $A_kB_kDC$ (or
$A_kB_kCD'$ ).    The segment $CD$ is the required one.  This construction also holds in the case when the point $C$ lies on
the straight line  $AB$ .

If it turns out that the point $A_i$ happens to lie on the
straight line  $A_{i-1}\ B_{i-2}$ , then it will be necessary to take
some other point instead of  $A_i$ .

C o n s t r u c t i o n  in the case when  $AB > R$ .  Making use of the solution of Problem 22, we construct points

$X_1, X_2, \ldots, X_n$ on the segment $AB$, satisfying $AX_1 \leqslant R$, $X_1 X_2 \leqslant R$, $\ldots, X_n B \leqslant R$.

We then construct parallelograms $AX_1 D_1 C$, $X_1 X_2 D_2 D_1$, $\ldots$, $X_{n-1} X_n D_n D_{n-1}$, $X_n BDD_n$. The segment $CD$ is the required one.

<u>Problem 24</u>. <u>To construct a segment equal to $\frac{1}{2^n}$ th of a given segment $AB$ in the case when $AB \geqslant 2R$ (to divide a segment into $2^n$ equal parts</u>).

C o n s t r u c t i o n. On the given segment $AB$, we find a point $C$ such that $AC \leqslant R$ (Problem 22). We construct the segment $AD = mAC$ (Problem 2) taking the number $m$ such, that $AD \leqslant AB$ and $DB < R$. In order to do that we repeat the segment $AC$ two, three, etc. times until we approach the point $B$. If, at the end, the number $m$ turns out to be odd, then we construct, in addition, the segment $DD_1 = AC$, then $AD_1 = (m+1)AC$, $AB < AD_1$ and $BD_1 < R$ (in Fig. 35, $m = 6$).

We bisect the segment $BD$ (or $BD_1$) at point $K$ (Problem 21, $BD < R$). We denote the midpoint of the segment $AD$ (or $AD_1$)

Fig. 35

by $E$, and we mark off the segment $EX_1$, equal and parallel to the segment $DK$ (Problem 23) in such a way, that $AX_1 = AE + EX_1$ (or $AX_1 = AE - EX_1$, if the point $E$ is the middle of the segment $AD_1$); to achieve that, we take the points $Q$, $M$, $Q_1$, $H$, ...and we construct parallelograms $QDKG$, $MQGN$, $Q_1 MNG_1$ and so on*.

The point $X_1$ bisects the given segment $AB$. After that, we bisect the segment $AX_1$ and we obtain a quarter of the segment $AB$ etc. If it happens that $AX_1 < 2R$, we use the construction indicated in Problem 21, otherwise we carry out

*The point $X_1$ will be constructed, if $AX_1 = AE + EX_1$ is constructed (see Note to Problem 6).

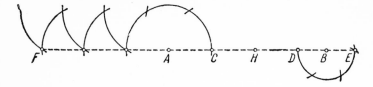

Fig. 36

the construction along lines similar to the above.

Problem 25. To construct a segment *n* times greater than the given segment *AB* in the case *AB > R*.

C o n s t r u c t i o n. On the given straight line *AB* we find a point *C* such that $AC < R$ (Problem 22). We construct the segment $AD = mAC$ (Problem 2, $AC < R$), picking the number *m* in such a way that $AD \leqslant AB$ and $DB < R$. In order to do this it is necessary to repeat the segment *AC* two, three, etc. times, until we reach the point *B*.

Towards the right of the point *D* we construct the segment $DE = nDB$ (Problem 2, $DB < R$). Finally, towards the left of the point *C* we construct the segment $AF = (n-1)mAC$ (the segment *CF* being equal to $[(n-1)m+1]CA$). The segment $FE = nAB$ is the required one. (In Fig. 36, $m = 3$, $n = 2$.)

P r o o f. The segment

$$FE = FA + AD + DE =$$
$$= (n-1) \ mAC + mAC + nDB = nmAC + nDB =$$
$$= n(mAC + DB) = n(AD + DB) = nAB.$$

N o t e. In order that the left end of the constructed segment should coincide with point *A*, it is necessary to mark off beforehand, to the right of the point *E*, the segment *EK*, equal and parallel to the segment *HD* $(AC = HD)$ (Problem 23) and then, in place of segment *AF*, to construct $EM = (n-1)mEK$. Then $AM = nAB$.

Problem 26. (The second basic operation). From a given centre *O*, to describe a circle of a given radius *AB*.

C o n s t r u c t i o n. If $AB \leqslant R$ then the circle can

E

be described directly by means of the given compasses with a
restricted opening. If $AB > R$, then we cannot draw a circle

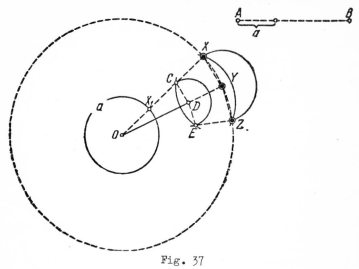

Fig. 37

in the form of a continuous curve with the given compasses.
However, in this case, any number of points can be constructed as close together as desired on the required circle,
whose centre and radius is given (Fig. 37).

We construct the segment $a = \frac{AB}{2^n}$ (Problems 21 and 24), taking the number $n$ such that $a \leqslant R$. We describe the circle
$(O, a)$, and take an arbitrary point $X_1$ on it and we construct
the segment $OX = 2^n OX_1$ (Problem 2, $OX_1 = a \leqslant R$ ). The
point $X$ lies on the circle $(O, AB)$. Varying the position
of point $X_1$ on the circumference $(O, a)$ it is possible to construct as many points of the required circumference as desired.
When the points $X$ and $Y$ of the required circumference are already constructed, and if $XY < R$, $DX \leqslant R$, then one can pro-
ceed to construct further points of the circumference as follows. We describe the circles $(D, C)$ and $(Y, C)$. At their intersection we obtain the point $E.$. If we then draw the circles
$(Z, Y)$ and $(E, Y)$, we shall have constructed one more point on
the circumference, and so on.

P r o o f.   The segment $OX = 2^n \cdot a = 2^n \cdot \frac{AB}{2^n} = AB$ .

Problem 27. (The third basic operation). To find the points of intersection of two given circles $(O, AB)$ and $(O_1, CD)$ .

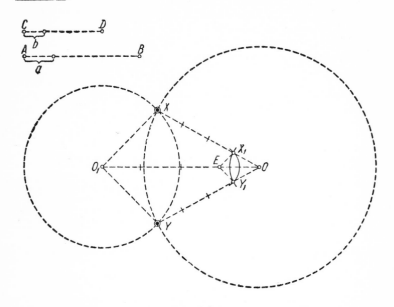

Fig. 38

C o n s t r u c t i o n. If the radii of both circles are no greater than $R$ , the construction of the points of intersection is carried out directly by means of the compasses.

Let us now suppose that the radius of one or both given circles is greater than $R$ .

We construct the segments $a = \frac{AB}{2^n}$, $b = \frac{CD}{2^n}$ and $OE = \frac{OO_1}{2^n}$ (Problems 21 and 24); we take the number $n$ such that $a \leqslant R$ and $b \leqslant R$ (Fig. 38).

We describe the circles $(O, a)$ and $(E, b)$ and we note their points of intersection, $X_1$ and $Y_1$ .

If we now construct the segments $OX^n = 2^n OX_1$ and $OY = 2^n OY_1$ , we obtain the required points of intersection $X$ and $Y$ of the given circles $(O, AB)$ and $(O_1, CD)$ .

P r o o f.

$$OX = 2^n \cdot a = 2^n \cdot \frac{AB}{2^n} = AB,$$

$$OY = 2^n \cdot \frac{AB}{2^n} = AB.$$

It follows from the similarity of triangles $OXO_1$ and $OX_1E$ $\left(\dfrac{OX}{OX_1} = \dfrac{OO_1}{OE} = 2^n \right.$ , the angle $O_1OX$ is common$\left.\right)$ that

$$O_1X = 2^n \cdot EX_1 = 2^n \cdot \frac{CD}{2^n} = CD.$$

In exactly the same way we obtain $O_1Y = CD$.

<u>Problem 28.</u>  <u>To construct the point $C_1$, symmetrical to a given point $C$, with respect to a given straight line $AB$.</u>

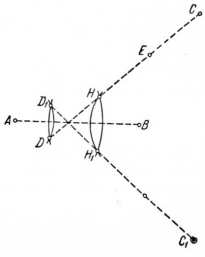

Fig. 39

Construction for the case $AC \leqslant R$ and $BC \leqslant R$ is given in Problem 1. If the distance of the point $C$ from the given straight line $AB$ is less than $R$, then, making use of Problem 22, it is possible to find points $A_1$ and $B_1$ on the straight line, such that $CA_1 \leqslant R$ and $CB_1 \leqslant R$. Now, let the distance of the point $C$ from the straight line $AB$ be greater than $R$. We can take $AB < 2R$; otherwise we can find such points on the given straight line using Problem 22.

We take an arbitrary point $E$ in the plane, such that $CE \leqslant R$ and the straight line $CE$ passes between the points $A$ and $B$. We construct the segment $CD = mCE$, for which we make $CE = \ldots$ $= HD$ (Problem 2). We pick the point $E$ and number $m$ in such a way that the segments $AD$, $AH$, $BD$ and $BH$ should not be greater than $R$.

We find points $D_1$ and $H_1$, symmetrical to points $D$ and $H$ with respect to the given straight line (Problem 1). We construct the segment $D_1C_1 = mD_1H_1$. The point $C_1$ is the required one, symmetrical to the given point $C$ with respect to the straight line $AB$ (Fig. 39).

The validity of the construction is obvious.

Problem 29. (The fourth basic operation). To find the points of intersection of a given circle $(O, CD)$ and a straight line, given by two points $A$ and $B$.

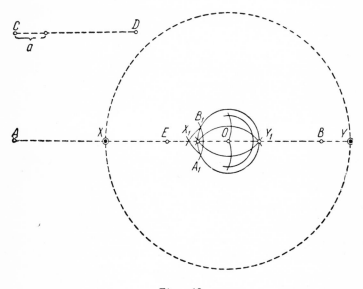

Fig. 40

C o n s t r u c t i o n in the case when the straight line does not pass through the centre of the circle.

We construct the point $O_1$ , symmetrical to the centre $O$ of the given circle with respect to the straight line $AB$ (Problem 28). We define the points of intersection $X$ and $Y$ of the circles $(O, CD)$ and $(O_1, CD)$ (Problem 27). The points $X$ and $Y$ are the required ones.

C o n s t r u c t i o n in the case when the straight line passes through the centre of the circle*(Fig. 40). We construct the segment $r = \frac{CD}{2^n}$ with the condition that $r \leqslant \frac{R}{2}$ (Problems 21 and 24). We describe the circle $(O, r)$ and we intersect it at points $A_1$ and $B_1$ by means of the circle $(A, d)$ or $(B, d)$ where $d$ is an arbitrary radius, less than or equal to $R$. When $d = R$, even if the circles $(B, R)$ or $(A, R)$ do not intersect the circle $(O, r)$ (in this case, $OA > R + r$ and $OB > R + r$ ), then using Problem 22 we find a point $E$ on the straight line $AB$ such that $OE < R + r$; the circle $(E, d)$ intersects $(O, r)$ in points $A_1$ and $B_1$ . By varying the size of radius $d$ , we should get the segment $a$ to equal $A_1B_1 \leqslant \frac{R}{2}$ .

We divide both arcs $A_1B_1$ of the circle $(O, r)$ in half at points $X_1$ and $Y_1$ (Problem 4). We construct segments $OX = 2^n OX_1$ and $OY = 2^n OY$ (Problem 2, $OX_1 = OY_1 = r \leqslant \frac{R}{2}$ ). Points $X$ and $Y$ are the required points of intersection of the given straight line and the given circle.

The largest circle drawn in this construction is drawn when the arc $A_1B_1$ is bisected. When an arc is divided in half (see Problem 4) the radius of the largest circle equals $BC = \sqrt{2a^2 + r^2}$ (see Fig. 5). In our construction that radius is $\sqrt{2a^2 + r^2} \leqslant \sqrt{2\left(\frac{R}{2}\right)^2 + \left(\frac{R}{2}\right)^2} < R$ .

Problem 30. To construct a segment, which is fourth pro-portional to three given segments   $a, b$  and  $c$ .

C o n s t r u c t i o n. If $a \leqslant R$, $b \leqslant R$ and $c \leqslant R$ , the construction is given in Problem 3. Now let at least

---

*To check this fact see note to Problem 1.

one of the above inequalities be invalid. We construct segments $a_1 = \frac{a}{2^n}$, $b_1 = \frac{b}{2^n}$ and $c_1 = \frac{c}{n}$ (Problems 21 and 24), picking natural numbers $n$ and $m$, such that $a_1 \leqslant R$, $b_1 \leqslant R$, $c_1 \leqslant R$ and $c_1 < 2a_1$.

We construct the segment $x_1$, the fourth proportional to the segments $a_1$, $b_1$ and $c_1$.

If we now construct the segment $x = 2^m x_1$ (Problems 2 and 25), we shall find the required segment, the fourth proportional of three given segments $a, b$ and $c$.

P r o o f. The proportion

$$\frac{a}{2^n} : \frac{b}{2^n} = \frac{c}{2^m} : x_1$$

can be written thus

$$a : b = c : 2^m x_1.$$

Problem 31. (The fifth basic operation). To construct the point of intersection of the given straight lines $AB$ and $CD$, each of which is defined by two points.

C o n s t r u c t i o n of the point of intersection of the given straight lines with compasses with a restricted opening can be carried out in the same way as in Problem 7, however, instead of Problems 1 and 3, we make use of Problems 28 and 30 respectively. To find point $E$ we apply Problem 27.

N o t e. Making use of Problem 22 we can take the points $A, B, C$ and $D$, which define the given straight lines so close to each other that all circles drawn in this construction will have radii not greater than $R$ and so can be drawn with compasses with a restricted opening of the legs.

On the basis of the discussion in this chapter we come to the following conclusion.

All five basic operations (simplest problems) can be carried out (solved) with compasses, describing circles whose radii do not exceed some prescribed length $R$.

Each geometrical construction problem  soluble by means

of compasses and a ruler  can always be reduced to carrying
out (in a certain order) a finite sequence of basic operations
(Section) I).

Thus, the following theorem holds.

T h e o r e m. <u>All geometrical construction problems</u>
<u>soluble by means of compasses and a ruler can be solved</u>
<u>exactly using only compasses capable of describing circles</u>
<u>whose radii do not exceed a certain prescribed length.</u>

We now investigate a general method of solving construction
problems by means of compasses  the opening of whose legs is
restricted from above by the segment $R$ .

Suppose that it is required to solve a certain construction
problem, soluble by means of compasses and a ruler, using
only compasses with a restricted opening. Let us imagine
this problem solved by means of compasses alone in the classical sense, using the compasses freely, when the opening of
the legs is not restricted in any way. As a result, we obtain a certain figure $\Phi$ , consisting of a finite number of
circles only. Let us denote the largest of the radii of all
the circles constituting the figure $\Phi$ by $R_1$ .

If it turns out that $R_1 \leqslant R$ , then the construction mentioned can be carried out by means of the given compasses
with a restricted opening of the legs.

Now, let $R_1 > R$ . Let us take a natural number $n$ , such
that $\frac{R_1}{2^n} \leqslant R$ . Now  if all the segments, including those
segments which define the radii of the given circles, were
made $2^n$ times smaller than they are, and the problem were
then solved by means of the given compasses, we should obtain the figure $\Phi_1'$ as a result. It will be similar to the
figure $\Phi$ , the coefficient of similarity being $\frac{1}{2^n}$ . All
the circles of figure $\Phi'$ can be drawn with the given com-
passes as their radii are no greater than  $\frac{R_1}{2^n} \left( \frac{R_1}{2^n} \leqslant R \right)$ .

It must be noted here, that if among the conditions of a
problem a certain figure $W$ is given in the plane of the drawing, then it is necessary to take one of the points of the
figure as the centre of similitude $O$ and to construct a
similar figure $W''$ with the coefficient of similarity $\frac{1}{2^n}$ (that

is, to make the figure $W$ $2^n$ times smaller).

Let us denote by $\Psi'$ that part of the figure $\Phi'$, which is
the required result. We construct the figure $\Psi$, similar
to the figure $\Psi'$ with centre of similitude $O$ and coefficient
of similarity $2^n$ (we make figure $\Psi'$, $2^n$ times larger), for
which we construct the segments

$$OX_1 = 2^n OX_1', \quad OX_2 = 2^n OX_2', \ldots, OX_k = 2^n OX_k,$$

where $X_1', X_2', \ldots, X_k'$ denote all points of intersection of the
circles in the figure $\Psi'$ and all the centres of these circles.
The points $X_1, X_2, \ldots, X_k$ of the figure $\Psi$ denote the centres
and points of intersection of the circles, which make up
that figure.

The figure $\Psi$ represents the required result of the solution
of the given problem. Straight lines and circles whose radii
are greater than $R$ cannot be drawn in figure with the given
compasses; they can be constructed in the form of points, as
close to each other as desired (Problems 22 and 26).

To illustrate the above arguments we give the solution of
Problem 27. In this solution $\Phi$ consists of circles $(O, AB)$
and $(O_1, CD)$. The given elements are two points $O$ and $O_1$ (representing the given figure $W$) and two segments $AB$ and $CD$.
The figure $\Phi'$ consists of circles $(O, a)$ and $(E, b)$ (together
with the centres $O$ and $E$ ).

The figure $\Psi'$, taken as the required result in the figure
$\Phi'$, consists of two points $X_1$ and $Y_1$. The required result
of the solution is the figure $\Psi$ consisting of points $X$ and
$Y$. $O$ is the centre of similitude (in Fig. 38, $2^n$ was taken
as 4 and $n$ as 2).

Usually in solving construction problems the number $n$ is
unknown, since we cannot construct figure $\Phi$ with the given
compasses, which means we cannot know the radius $R_1$ of the
largest of the circles. Taking this circumstance into
account we carry out the solution of the problem with the
given compasses (with a restricted opening) until we come to
a circle with the radius $r_1 > R$. We select the natural num-
ber $n_1$ in such a way that $\frac{r_1}{2^{n_1}} \leqslant R$. We diminish the given
segments $2^{n_1}$ times and we begin the solution of the given
problem anew; as a result we shall either solve the problem

completely and construct the figure $\Phi'$ , or we shall again
arrive at a circle of radius $r_2 > R$ . We select the natural
number $n_2 \left( \frac{r_2}{2^{n_2}} \leqslant R \right)$ and again we diminish the segments $2^{n_2}$
times and so on. After a finite number of steps the figure
$\Phi'$ will be constructed.

Using the general method of solution, it is easy to construct by means of compasses with a restricted opening the
inverse figures of a point, a straight line or a circle.

In concluding this section we examine the solution of the
following problem.

<u>Problem 32</u>. <u>To divide the given segment</u> $AB = a$ <u>into five</u>
<u>equal parts, if we cannot have a segment five times as large</u>
<u>as</u> $AB$ .

In the extensive work of Mascheroni ('The Geometry of Compasses') this problem is the only one solved with the restric-
tion indicated in its conditions.

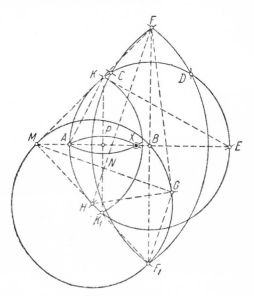

Fig. 41

C o n s t r u c t i o n. We describe the circle $(B, A)$ and we make $AC = CD = DE = a$ (Fig. 41). We draw the circles $(A, D)$ and $(E, C)$ until they meet at the points $F$ and $F_1$ . We mark the point $H$ of intersection of the circle $(F_1, AB)$ with the circle $(B, A)$ . We then describe the circles $(H, F_1)$ and $(F, AE)$ and at their intersection we obtain the point $G$. On the circle $(B, A)$ we mark off the chords $AK = AK_1 = F_1G$. If we draw the circles $(K, A)$ and $(K_1, A)$ , their point of intersection is the required point $X$ . The segment $BX = \frac{1}{5} AB$ .

P r o o f. Let the point $M$ on the circle $(H, F_1)$ be diametrically opposite to the point $F_1$ and let the point $N$ be the point of intersection of the straight lines $HF$ and $MG$. The segment $BF = BF_1 = \sqrt{2}\,AB$. The length of the tangent from the point $F$ to the circle $(H, F_1)$ is equal to

$$b = \sqrt{FF_1 \cdot FB} = \sqrt{2\,\sqrt{2}\,AB \cdot \sqrt{2}\,AB} = 2AB.$$

But, on the other hand, $FG = 2AB$ ; this means that the straight line $FG$ touches the circle $(H, F_1)$ at the point $G$ .

From the right-angled triangle $FGH$ we have

$$HF = \sqrt{HG^2 + GF^2} = \sqrt{5}\,AB.$$

The triangle $FMF_1$ is isosceles, since the angle $F_1BM$ is a right angle, supported by the diameter $F_1M$ of the circle $(H, F_1)$ . This means that $MF_1 = MF = 2AB$ .

The triangle $MGF$ is also isosceles $(MF = FG = 2\,AB)$, therefore $MG$ is perpendicular to $HF$ .

From the right-angled triangle $HGF$ , whose altitude is the segment $GN$, we obtain

$$HG^2 = a^2 = HF \cdot HN = \sqrt{5}\,a \cdot HN$$

or

$$HN = \frac{a}{\sqrt{5}}.$$

From the right-angled triangles $HNG$ and $MGF_1$, we find

$$NG = \sqrt{a^2 - \left(\frac{a}{\sqrt{5}}\right)^2} = \frac{2a}{\sqrt{5}} = \frac{1}{2}\,MG,$$
$$GF_1^2 = 4a^2 - \frac{16a^2}{5} = \frac{4a^2}{5}.$$

and, finally, from the right-angled triangle $AKE$ we have

$$AK^2 = GF_1^2 = AE \cdot AP = 2AB \cdot \frac{AX}{2} = AX \cdot AB,$$

or

$$AX = \frac{GF_1^2}{a} = \frac{4a}{5}.$$

Hence

$$BX = \frac{1}{5} AB.$$

# 6. CONSTRUCTIONS BY MEANS OF COMPASSES ALONE, WITH THE ANGLE RESTRICTED FROM BELOW

In this chapter we shall make use of compasses the opening of whose legs is restricted only from below by the prescribed lengths $R_{min}$ . With such compasses it is possible to draw circles of any radius greater than or equal to the segment $R_{min}$ . In the following, we shall simply write $R$ instead of $R_{min}$ .

Problem 33. To construct a segment $n$ times as large as a given segment $AA_1$ .

C o n s t r u c t i o n. We construct the segment $A_1E$ perpendicular to the given segment $AA_1$ (Problem 8, we take $OA \geqslant R$ ). We define the point $E'$ , symmetrical to the point $E$ with respect to the straight line $AA_1$ (Problem 1, here $AE > R$ and $A_1E > R$ ). We construct the point $A_2$ , symmetrical to the point $A$ with respect to the straight line $EE'$. The segment $AA_2 = 2AA_1$ (Fig. 42).

We then describe the circle $(E, A)$ and we mark off chords $AB_1 = B_1C_1 = C_1E_1$ equal to the radius. The segment $A_2E_1$ is perpendicular to $AA_2$ . We find the point $E_1'$ , symmetrical to the point $E_1$ with respect to the straight line $AA_2$. If we now construct points $A_3$ and $A_4$ , symmetrical to points $A_1$ and $A$ respectively, we have

$$AA_3 = 3AA_1, \quad AA_4 = 4AA_1.$$

Further construction is repeated similarly. If $AA_1 \geqslant R$ , then the construction is given in Problem 2.

The radii of all the circles drawn in this construction are not less than the segment $R$ .

N o t e. From the demonstrated construction it is obvious that the points $A_2, A_4, A_8, A_{16}, \ldots$ can be constructed straight away, missing out the construction of the points $A_3, A_5, A_6, A_7, A_9, \ldots$ i.e. the segments 2, 4, 8, 16, $\ldots$, $2^n$ times as large as the given segment $AA_1$ can be found immediately.

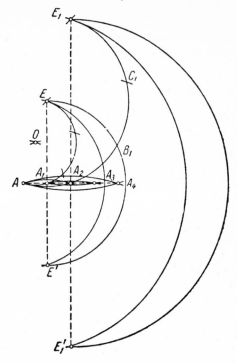

Fig. 42

Problem 34. To construct a segment equal to $\frac{1}{n}$ th of the given segment $AB$ (i.e. to divide a segment into $n$ equal parts).

C o n s t r u c t i o n. If $AB \geqslant R$ , then the construction is given in Problem 9.

Now, let $AB < R$ . We construct the segment $AB' = mAB$ (Problem 33) and we take such a natural number $m$ , that $AB' \geqslant R$ . We divide the segment into $n \cdot m$ equal parts (Problem 9). We shall obtain the required segment $AX = \frac{AB'}{n \cdot m}$ .

Indeed, $AX = \frac{AB'}{n \cdot m} = \frac{mAB}{n \cdot m} = \frac{AB}{n}$ .

N o t e:  In this case, if we apply the construction of
Problem 10 instead of Problem 9, we obtain the segment
$AX = \frac{1}{2^n} AB$ .

The solution of Problem 5 is also suitable for compasses
with opening restricted from below.

Problem 35 .   The second basic operation . Using the point
O as centre, to describe a circle of radius  $AB = r$  .

C o n s t r u c t i o n.  If $AB \geqslant R$ , then the circle can
be drawn directly. If $AB < R$ then we cannot describe the
circle as a continuous curve with the given compasses; in
this case it is possible to construct any number of points
situated as closely together as desired on the circumference
of the circle defined given by its centre and radius.

Let  $AB < R$ . With an arbitrary radius   $a > R + r$ we describe the circles $(O, a)$ and $(A, a)$ and we take two points $C$
and $D$ on the second circle, such that $CD \geqslant R$ . If, now, we
mark off the chord  $C_1 D_1 = CD$  on the circle $(O, a)$ and we describe the circles $(C_1, CB)$ and $(D_1, DB)$ , we obtain at their
intersection the point $X$ , which lies on the required circle
$(O, r)$ . By varying the position of the chord $C_1 D_1$ of the
circle $(O, a)$ it is possible to construct any desired number
of points of the required circle.

The truth of the construction described follows immediately
from the congruence of the triangles $ACD = OC_1 D_1$  and  $BCD = XC_1 D_1$

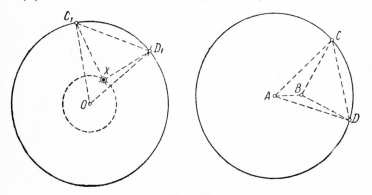

Fig. 43

We shall now indicate a general method of solving geometrical construction problems using only compasses whose opening is restricted from below by the length $R$. By this method it is possible to solve every construction problem  soluble by means of compasses and a ruler, including the third, fourth and fifth basic problems.

The general method of solving problems with compasses which describe circles of radius not less than $R$ coincides with the general method of solving problems described in Section 5.

The difference between these methods lies in the fact that the segments given in the conditions of the problem have not to be diminished $2^n$ times but, quite the reverse, increased $n$ times (or $2^n$ times) (Problem 33). After that, we have to construct the figure $\Phi'$, which is similar to figure $\Phi$ and $n$ times as large as it. The number $n$ is picked in such a way that all the circles of figure $\Phi'$ have radii larger than $R$ and therefore can be described with the given compasses $\left(nR_1 \geqslant R \right.$, where $R_1$ is the radius of the smallest circle of figure $\Phi \left. \right)$.

The figure $\Psi$, representing the required result of solving the problem, is constructed $n$ times less than the figure $\Psi'$ (Problem 34). Thus we arrive at the following theorem.

T h e o r e m. <u>All geometrical construction problems soluble by means of compasses and a ruler can be solved exactly using only compasses which describes circles whose radii are not less than a certain prescribed length.</u>

## 7. CONSTRUCTIONS USING ONLY COMPASSES WITH CONSTANT OPENING OF LEGS

Geometric constructions with compasses with a constant opening of the legs, with which it is possible to describe only circles of fixed radius $R$ , were investigated by many scholars. A large part of the work 'The Book of Geometrical Constructions' of the Arab mathematician Abu Yaf is devoted to this subject. Leonardo da Vinci, Cardano, Tartaglia, Ferrari and others have occupied themselves with solving construction problems using only compasses with a constant opening.

By means of compasses with a constant opening equal to $R$ we can raise a perpendicular at one end of the segment $AB$, only if $AB < 2R$ (Problem 8); we can make a segment 2, 3, 4, ... times as large as a given one (Problem 2). If $AB < 2R$ and $AB \neq R$ it is possible to construct the points of a straight line $AB$ (Problem 5) altering the position of the symmetrical points $C$ and $C_1$ each time. We cannot, however, divide segments and arcs into equal parts, find proportional segments and so on, with these compasses.

Thus, it is impossible to solve all construction problems, soluble by means of compasses and a ruler, using only compasses with a constant opening.

Taking into account results obtained in Sections 5-7, it is necessary to note that at the moment the question of the possibility of solving geometrical construction problems by means of compasses with a restricted opening of the legs from above and from below simultaneously, i.e. with compasses describing circles of radius not smaller than $R_{min}$ and not greater than $R_{max}$ , remains open. What problems can be solved with the help of such compasses? Is it possible to solve all construction problems soluble by means of compasses and a ruler with them?

If it is, can the difference $R_{max} - R_{min}$ be made as small as desired? In other words, is it possible to solve all

F

construction problems, soluble by means of compasses and a ruler, by the help of compasses with a 'nearly' constant opening alone? As has already been noted at the beginning of this chapter, all these problems cannot be solved by means of compasses with a constant opening*.

It seems to us that the following problems, as yet hardly discussed in the literature, are not without interest.

1. The investigation of solving geometrical construction problems by means of compasses with a restricted opening (from above only, or from below only, or from above and below at the same time) and with a ruler of a constant length. The indication of the simplest methods of construction.

2. Examination of geometrical constructions by means of a ruler alone (constructions of Steiner), when an auxiliary circle $(O, R)$ is given in the plane of the drawing and the ruler has a constant length $l$. Here, the cases $l < R$ and $l > R$ are important.

---

*For carrying out geometrical constructions, $k$ compasses might be given, each of which has an opening restricted simultaneously from below and from above. The opening of the first compasses might be restricted by the lengths $r_1$, and $R_1$, of the second one by lengths $r_2$ and $R_2$, ... of the $k$th one by the lengths $r_k$ and $R_k$, $k = 1, 2, 3, \ldots$ .

## 8. CONSTRUCTIONS WITH COMPASSES ALONE ON CONDITION THAT ALL CIRCLES PASS THROUGH THE SAME POINT

In this section we shall consider the solution of geometrical construction problems with compasses alone on condition that all circles that are drawn pass through one point in the plane*.

D e f i n i t i o n. The angle of intersection of two circles (in general of two curves) is understood to be the angle made by the tangents to the circles (curves) at their points of intersection. The circles are said to be orthogonal if they intersect at right angles.

T h e o r e m   1. If the circle $(O, R)$ intersects the circle of inversion $(O, r)$ orthogonally, then it is its own inverse**.

P r o o f. If the circles intersect orthogonally, then the angle $OAO_1$ formed by their radii at the intersection of the circles is a right angle. This means that the straight line $OA$ is a tangent to the circle $(O,R)$ at the point $A$, and

$$OP \cdot OP' = OA^2 = r^2.$$

The last equation is true for any secant $OP$. The point $P'$ is the inverse of the point $P$. The arc $APA_1$ of the circle $(O_1, R)$ is the inverse of the arc $AP'A_1$ (Fig. 44).

In Problem 11 we were given the construction of a segment $3^n$ times as large as a given segment $AA_0$. In carrying out this construction all circles pass through the point $A$. The only exception is the circle $(A, A_0)$ which is drawn in order to define the points $E$ and $E'$ when the chords $AE = EC$ and $AE' = E'C'$ are drawn. The circle $(A, A_0)$, however, does not need to be drawn, but the following steps can be taken.

---

*In this section no restrictions are put on the extent of the opening of the compasses.
**The converse theorem is also true but it will not be used in this chapter.

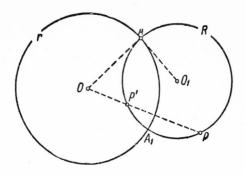

Fig. 44

We make the opening of the compasses equal to $AA_0$ and we place the point of the pencil at the point $A$ , then, without changing the opening of the compasses we set them up in such a way that the sharp end of the needle falls on the arc of the circle $(A_0, A)$ . The sharp end of the needle of the compasses will rest at point $E$ or $E'$ . If we now describe the circle $(E, A)$ , then at its intersection with the circle $(A_0, A)$ we have constructed the point $C$ . In just the same way it is possible to construct the point $C'$ .

And so it is possible to construct a segment $3^n$ times as large as a given one (Problem 11) in such a way that all circles pass through the same point.

The solutions of Problems 15, 16, 17 are found in such a way (see Figs. 26, 28, 29) that all circles pass through the same point $O$ - the centre of inversion.

In the construction of the point $X$ , which is the inverse of point $C$ in the case $OC \leqslant \frac{r}{2}$ (Problem 15), in order that all drawn circles without exception should pass through the one point $O$ , it is necessary to construct the segment $OC_1 = 3^n \cdot OC > \frac{r}{2}$ (Problem 11, account being taken of remarks made at the beginning of this section) instead of the segment $OC_1 = nOC_1 > \frac{r}{2}$ (Fig. 27) and to construct $OX = 3^n \cdot OC_1'$ .

Thus, with the help of compasses alone, it is possible to construct the inverse of a given point, to construct a circle passing through the centre of inversion, the inverse of a given straight line, and to construct a straight line which is the inverse of the circle that passes through $O$ , drawing all circles through the same point $O$ the centre of inversion.

As we noted in the Introduction, Steiner showed that all construction problems, soluble by means of a ruler and compasses, can also be solved by means of a ruler alone, if in the plane of the drawing there is a given constant (auxiliary) circle $(O_1, R)$ and its centre.

Now, let us suppose that a certain construction problem was solved by Steiner's method; as a result we shall obtain a figure $\Phi$ in the plane of the drawing, consisting apart from the auxiliary circle of straight lines only. Let us take an arbitrary circle $(O, r)$, the only condition being that its centre $O$ does not lie on the circle $(O_1, R)$ and does not lie on any of the straight lines of figure $\Phi$ and let us take it as the circle of inversion. We construct the figure $\Phi'$ which is the inverse of figure $\Phi$ . The figure $\Phi'$ so constructed will consist of circles only, all of which (with the exception of two: the circle of inversion $(O, r)$ and the circle, inverse of $(O_1, R)$ ) will pass through the same point $O$ - the centre of inversion.

If the circle of inversion $(O, r)$ intersects the auxiliary circle $(O_1, R)$ at a right angle then, by Theorem 1, the circle $(O_1, R)$ is self-inverse. The figure $\Phi$ consists of straight lines, the circle $(O_1, R)$ and, perhaps, some isolated points; the inverse figure $\Phi'$ consists of the circle $(O_1, R)$, circles passing through the centre of inversion $O$ , inverse of the straight lines and, perhaps, some isolated points. To construct the figure $\Phi'$ it is necessary to make use of Problems 15 and 16 only.

Thus, in the construction of figure $\Phi'$ , the inverse of figure $\Phi$ , in the case when the circle of inversion intersects the auxiliary circle at right angles, all circles, including the circles with whose help $\Phi'$ is constructed, will pass through the same point $O$ , there being only two exceptions: the circle of inversion $(O, r)$ and the circle $(O_1, R)$ .

In order to illustrate the above, we shall solve the following problem.

**Problem 36.** The circle $(O, R)$ and a point $A$ on it are given. To drop a perpendicular from the given point $C$ to the straight line $O_1A$ by means of a ruler alone.

C o n s t r u c t i o n. We draw the straight line $O_1A$ and produce it to intersect the given circle at the point $B$. We draw the straight lines $AC$ and $BC$ and mark the points $E$ and $D$ of their intersection with the circle $(O_1, R)$. If we now draw the straight lines $AD$ and $BE$ until they meet at the point $F$, then the straight line $CF$ will be perpendicular to the straight line $O_1A$. Let us denote the foot of the perpendicular by $H$ (Fig. 45).

P r o o f. The segments $CD$ and $EF$ are the altitudes of the triangle $AFC$, since the angles $ADB$ and $AEB$ are right angles, therefore $FC$ is perpendicular to $AB$, as the three altitudes of the triangle intersect each other at one point $B$.

The figure $\Phi$ in this problem consists of the circle $(O_1, R)$ and six straight lines $AB$, $AC$, $AD$, $CD$, $CF$ and $EF$. First we arrange the point $O$ and the radius $r$ so as to cause the

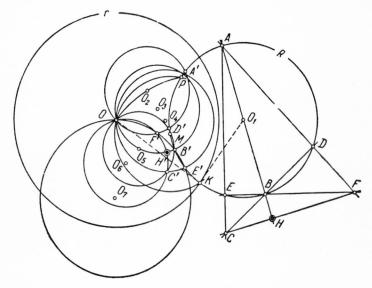

Fig. 45

circles $(O, r)$ and $(O_1, R)$ to intersect orthogonally. To do
this we make use of the solution of Problem 8 (Second Method);
we take two random points $K$ and $M$ on the circle $(O_1, R)$ and we
construct $KO$ perpendicular to $KO_1$ (Problem 8) for which we
draw the circles $(M, K)$ and $(P, K)$ until they meet at the point
$O$ (Fig. 45). The point $P$ is obtained at the intersection
of the circles $(M, K)$ and $(O_1, R)$.

Varying the position of the points $K$ and $M$ it is possible
to construct a point $O$  which does not lie on any of the
straight lines of figure $\Phi$. The circle $(O, K)$ intersects
the given circle $(O_1, R)$ at a right angle, and can be taken
as the circle of inversion  $OK = r$.

The figure  $\Phi'$, inverse of the figure $\Phi$, consists of
seven circles $(O_2, O)$, $(O_3, O)$, $(O_4, O)$, $(O_5, O)$, $(O_6, O)$, $(O_7, O)$ and
$(O_1, R)$ [the circle $(O_1, R)$ is self-inverse]. The first six
circles pass through the centre of inversion $O$ and they are
correspondingly inverse to the straight lines $AF$, $AB$, $AE$, $CD$,
$CF$ and $EF$ of figure $\Phi$. The points $A'$, $B'$, $C',D'$, $E'$, $F'$ and $H'$
of the figure $\Phi$ are inverse of the points $A$, $B$, $C$, $D$, $E$, $F$ and
$H$ respectively. All circles drawn to construct the first
six circles of figure $\Phi'$, and also the circles $(M, K)$ and
$(K, P)$ drawn to define the centre of inversion $O$, pass
through the same point $O$ in the plane.

Hence we have the theorem:

T h e o r e m   2. <u>Every geometrical construction problem,</u>
<u>soluble by means of compasses and a ruler, can be solved by</u>
<u>means of compasses alone in such a way that all circles of</u>
<u>the construction, except two, the circle of inversion and the</u>
<u>auxiliary circle of Steiner, pass through the same point –</u>
<u>the centre of inversion $O$.</u>

Now, let a certain problem be solved by Steiner's method.
As a result we obtain the figure $\Phi$ consisting of the circle
$(O_1, R)$ and straight lines, some of which pass through the
centre $O$. If the auxiliary circle $(O_1, R)$ be taken as the
circle of inversion, and the figure $\Phi'$, inverse of $\Phi$, be
constructed, then the constructed figure $\Phi'$ will consist of
straight lines and circles, all these straight lines and
circles passing through one and the same predetermined point*.

---

*Adler [1] states (Chapter XX) that, if the auxiliary circle
of Steiner  $(O_1, R)$ is taken as the circle of inversion, then
'Not only is it possible, as had been shown by Mascheroni,

Hence a theorem.

T h e o r e m   3.  <u>Every geometric construction problem
can always be solved by means of a ruler and compasses in
such a way   that all straight lines and circles   except one
(the circle of inversion) pass through one predetermined
point - the centre of inversion.</u>

Suppose now that in the solution of geometrical construction problems by means of compasses alone the use of a ruler
is permitted once. (Or let us suppose, that the straight
line $AB$ has been drawn by means of a ruler in the plane of
the drawing.) Let us take an arbitrary circle $(O, r)$ with
centre $O$ , not on the straight line $AB$ , as the circle of
inversion, and let us construct the circle $(O_1, R)$ , inverse
of the given straight line (Problem 16). The circle $(O_1, R)$
passes through the centre of inversion $O$ and $R = OO_1$ .

The solution of any problem on construction by Steiner's
method, with an auxiliary circle $(O_1, R)$ gives the figure $\Phi$,
consisting only of straight lines and the circle $(O_1, R)$ ;
the inverse figure $\Phi'$ will consist, apart from the straight
line $AB$, of circles only, passing through the centre of
inversion $O$ . At the same time we presuppose  that none of
the straight lines of the solution by Steiner's method had
passed through the point $O$ , lying on the auxiliary circle
$(O_1, R)$  , otherwise another circle should be taken as the
circle of inversion $(O, r)$ .

If the straight line $AB$ has not been drawn, but the single
use of a ruler is permitted, then we take an arbitrary circle
$(O_1, R)$ in the plane of the drawing as an auxiliary and we

---

to solve all geometrical construction problems of the
second degree with the exclusive use of compasses, but it
is possible to add the condition, that all circles included
in the construction, except one of them, should pass through
the same arbitrarily selected point'.

The error of this statement follows from the fact that all
construction problems, soluble by means of compasses and a
ruler, are incapable of being solved by means of a ruler
alone, if the centre of the auxiliary circle $O$  is unknown,
i.e. if no straight lines are passed through the centre $O$
[the lines being self-inverse (Theorem 2, Section 3) and,
therefore, belonging to figure $\Phi'$].

solve the given problem by Steiner's method. Then we take
an arbitrary point $O$ on the circumference of that circle,
on condition that it should not lie on any of the straight
lines of the figure $\Phi$. With the radius $r < 2R$, we describe
the circle $(O, r)$ and we mark its points of intersection with
the circle $(O_1, R)$ by $A$ and $B$. We take the ruler and draw
the straight line $AB$, which is the inverse of the circle
$(O_1, R)$ if we regard $(O, r)$ as the circle of inversion.

Then we construct figure $\Phi'$, the inverse of figure $\Phi$.

T h e o r e m  4. If a straight line is drawn in the
plane of the drawing, then all construction problems, soluble
by means of compasses and a ruler can be solved by means of
compasses alone in such a way that all circles of this construction, except one (the circle of inversion) will pass
through the same point of the plane.

This theorem is to a certain extent analogous to the basic
theorem of Steiner for constructions with a ruler alone with
a constant circle.

Now, let there be drawn in the plane of the drawing by
means of a ruler a certain figure $\Psi$ consisting of straight
lines and segments (for instance, two parallel lines or a
parallelogram and so on).

Let us suppose that we solved a certain construction problem by Steiner's method taking the figure $\Psi$ as an auxiliary
one. As a result we obtain a certain figure $\Phi$ consisting of
straight lines only. The figure $\Psi$ is a part of the figure
$\Phi$.

Let us take an arbitrary circle $(O, r)$ on condition that
its centre does not lie on any of the straight lines of the
figure $\Phi$, as the circle of inversion, and let us construct
the figure $\Phi'$, inverse of the figure $\Phi$. The figure $\Phi'$ will
consist of circles, passing only through one point $O$ - the
centre of inversion.

T h e o r e m  5. If a certain figure in the plane is
given, consisting only of straight lines and segments, then
all construction problems which can be solved by Steiner's
method, taking this figure as an auxiliary one, can always
be solved by means of compasses alone in such a way that

all circles   except one (the circle of inversion) pass
through one and the same point, taken at random in the plane
of the drawing.

# REFERENCES

1. A. ADLER, Theory of Geometric Construction (Teoriya geometricheskikh postroyenii), Odessa (1924).

2. I.I. ALEKSANDROV, Collection of Problems on Geometrical Constructions (Sbornik geometricheskikh zadach na postroyeniye), Moscow (1950).

3. B.I. ARGUNOV and M.B. BLANK, Plane Geometrical Constructions (Geometricheskiye postroyeniya na ploskosti), Moscow (1955).

4. A.M. VORONETS, Geometry of the Circle (Geometriya tsirkulya), Moscow (1934).

5. S.I. ZETEL', Geometry of the Line and Circle (Geometriya lineiki i geometriya tsirkulya), Moscow (1950).

6. A.N. KOSTOVSKII, On the possibility of solving geometrical construction problems by means of compasses alone with the opening of the legs restricted. Nauk. zap. L'viv. derzhuniv., 24 (1954).

7. A.N. KOSTOVSKII, The solution of geometrical construction problems by means of compasses alone with a fixed angle. Pit. mekh. i mat. L'viv. derzhuniv., 44 (1957).

8. B.V. KUTUZOV, Geometry (Geometriya), Moscow (1955).

9. R. COURANT and H. ROBBINS, What is Mathematics? New York (1941).

10. L. MASCHERONI, La Geometria del Composso, Pavia (1797).

11. Ye.Ya. ASTRYAB and S.O. SMOGORZHEVSKII (editors), Method for the Solution of Geometrical Construction Problems in Secondary Schools (Metodika roz'vyazuvannya zadach na pobudovu v serednii shkoli), Kiev (1940).

12. I.F. TESLENKO, The Inversion Method and its Applications (Metod inversii ta iogo zastosuvannya), Kiev (1954).

13. G. RADEMACHER and O. TÖPLITZ, Numbers and Figures (Chisla i figury), Ob. nauch. tekh. izd. (1936).